Kingston Hospital.

[Incorporated by Act of Parliament—144 Beds.]

Admit Mr Alfred Sales Oliver

During the hours of Medical attendance.

PERPETUAL.

Ja. S. Sampson

Prest. Board Governors K.H.

James Hopkirk

Secretary.

Kingston 1st Nov. 1857

Kingston General Hospital

Margaret Angus

Published for the Kingston General Hospital
by MCGILL-QUEENS UNIVERSITY PRESS
Montreal and London, 1973

Kingston General Hospital

A Social and Institutional History

©McGill-Queen's University Press 1973
ISBN 0 7735 0173 8
Library of Congress Catalog Card No. 72-97726
Legal Deposit 1st Quarter 1973
Design: Peter Dorn, MGDC
Typesetting: Paramount Typesetting Co. Ltd.
Printing: University of Toronto Press

PRINTED IN CANADA

Contents

List of illustrations

This is the story of the Kingston General Hospital – how it came to be established and how it has grown. The growth is measured not only in buildings, machines, and staff but also in knowledge, skills, and service. And since a hospital cannot develop in isolation, the story is told in relation to the people, the times, and the development of medical knowledge and practice. The hospital represents a common ground on which the patient, the community, and the professional groups meet.

Kingston General Hospital is strongly rooted in the community. It began as a hostel, supported by private charity, to provide food and shelter for the sick poor. With the advancement of medical knowledge and the growth of social consciousness, together with economic change, the treatment of the sick poor, and indeed of all the sick, became the responsibility of government. Meanwhile, Kingston General Hospital maintained and broadened its community role. Furthermore, it has developed service, teaching, and research to become one of the major teaching hospitals of Canada. Queen's University, too, came to have an increasingly important association with the Hospital. The role it has played in Hospital affairs is a reflection of its contribution to medical education and to the community.

In the Board of Governors – volunteers dedicated to the interests of the Hospital – the concept of Kingston General Hospital as a true community hospital has always been most faithfully realized. They have had the responsibility for major decisions and have been accountable to the Government for the discharge of that responsibility. The words 'the Board decided' which appear so many times in this history cannot possibly indicate the many hours they spent in serious consideration before the decisions were reached. The Governors' contribution to the Hospital and to the community is immeasurable.

The story of the buildings is more easily told and more tangible than is the story of the care provided and comfort given in those buildings. Dramatic moments in surgery and major developments in medicine excite more interest than do the hours in committee and the decisions which made possible the facilities for those achievements. Stories of the great dedication and prolonged service by many individuals would include not only those of administrators – both voluntary and paid – of doctors and nurses, but also of stewards, clerks, cooks, maids, and handymen. A few individual stories must be taken as representative of the many.

Events of the early years fall easily into a pattern; the span of years has filtered out the less important. The accelerated pace of change in recent years makes it difficult to view the most recent of them in what may come to be the proper perspective. What seems important at the time of writing may not be so in time to come. The emphasis may change but the events themselves are here recorded.

Margaret Angus, Kingston Ontario

Foreword The Board of Governors of the Kingston General Hospital takes great pride in the publication of the history of the hospital.

It is appropriate that the publication of this book which portrays an important facet of the history of our community should coincide with Kingston's Tercentenary. It is also both appropriate and timely that it should cover the years from 1832 to 1972 – that span of 140 years from the date of the first grant of £3,000 made by the Government to 'aid in the erection of a hospital in or near the town of Kingston' up to the present day.

Today the Kingston General Hospital stands at the beginning of a new era. We are moving into closer association with the Hotel Dieu Hospital, St. Mary's of the Lake Hospital, Kingston Psychiatric Hospital, Ongwanada Hospital, Queen's University, and the St. Lawrence College of Applied Arts and Technology to form the Kingston Health Sciences Complex, an integrated system of health care delivery to meet today's community needs. This new era will mean significant changes for our hospital. A history of former problems and accomplishments will provide a valuable record of the past and an inspiration for the future.

When we decided to commission a history of the Kingston General Hospital, we were indeed fortunate to find for the task an historian of the calibre and reputation of Mrs. Margaret Angus. We would like to express our thanks to her for the quality of her work, to Professor Gundy for his editorial advice, to the members of the hospital staff and the community who provided materials and assistance, and to our Governors and Medical Staff whose generous support helped to make the publication possible.

We hope that this book will be a source of information, inspiration, and pleasure to its readers.

Harvey L. Millman,
President, Board of Governors,
Kingston General Hospital, 1971–73

My first acknowledgement must be to the Board of Governors for giving me access *Acknowledge-* to the Hospital records and for generously supporting this work. It was an honour *ments* to be asked to prepare this history.

I am especially indebted to Mr. Donald MacIntyre, former Executive Director, who put at my disposal the Hospital records and a place to work on them. He read the manuscript and made very useful comments, as did Mr. John J. MacKay, a past president of the Board of Governors. I wish to thank, too, Dr. D. L. Wilson for his constructive criticism and his enthusiastic interest as the work progressed.

Mrs. Faith Avis, the Hospital's public relations officer, also read the manuscript, and during the three years I worked on this history was a constant source of information and encouragement.

To all those administrators and doctors who so willingly answered my questions and lent me material, I express my deep appreciation. Mr. Fraser Armstrong, former Superintendent, and Dr. W. Ford Connell, former Chief of Medicine, were especially helpful in providing information not contained in the records. I am glad to acknowledge the assistance and interest also of Miss Louise Acton, Miss Olevia Wilson, and of Doctors W. A. Campbell, Frederick Cays, D. C. Matheson, G. W. Mylks, E. P. White, and the late Dr. Stuart Houston. Dr. M. W. Partington's interest and care in assembling Hospital records fortunately saved some of them from disposal.

Miss Virginia Parker, Health Sciences Librarian, and Mr. Ian Wilson, Queen's Archivist, cheerfully encouraged my researches. The Department of the History of Medicine at McGill University, and the Baldwin Room of the Toronto Public Library answered queries about Dr. James Sampson. Old pictures, reports, and clippings have come from many people – Mr. Fred Buck, Mrs. M. Archer, Miss Jessie Orr, among others.

My husband served as a rather exacting critic and constructive reader, and with my friend and editor, H. Pearson Gundy, deserves much of the credit for what clarity of presentation I may have achieved.   M.A.

One

The history of the Kingston General Hospital in a sense goes back in time to the beginning of British settlement in Kingston. The British, like the French before them, recognizing the importance of this location, placed here their main fortifica- tions on the water route to Upper Canada. As settlement progressed, Kingston, the main port for the influx of men and materials into Upper Canada, became the centre for the medical treatment of immigrants and transients.

The founding of the Kingston General Hospital was a logical step in the development of health care in Kingston. When the Loyalists and disbanded regiments were settled in this district in 1783 and 1784, under the aegis of the military authorities, their medical needs were met by surgeons Connor, Latham and Sparham, attached as hospital mates or surgeons to British regiments stationed at Cataraqui (Kingston). Among the Loyalists there was one surgeon, Dr. Robert Kerr, acting hospital mate to Sir John Johnson's 2nd Battalion, who was in Kingston before he moved on to Niagara.

Military rule ended in 1788, when the government of the districts was handed over to magistrates working through the Courts of Quarter Sessions. The care of the sick poor then became the responsibility of the Town Wardens. Yet Kingston as a naval base and garrison town continued to be well supplied with competent medical men and the civilian population benefited from the private practice of naval and military surgeons. Since those surgeons had been trained in the great British hospitals in London, Edinburgh, Aberdeen, and Dublin, the quality of medical care was high for that period. And as officers of high social standing in the community, they had a long-range effect on the public and political position of the profession in Upper Canada and especially in Kingston.

To maintain the standard of medical care, the first Upper Canada statute to 'Regulate the Practice of Physic and Surgery' was enacted in 1795. It provided for the appointment of two examiners to ascertain the fitness of candidates to practice medicine. Dr. James Macaulay, Principal Surgeon of H.M. Hospital at Kingston, was in charge. Since there was as yet no medical training in Upper Canada, they examined the authenticity of licences issued elsewhere. Constant and competent medical care was available only in the larger settlements. The rural population, therefore, was dependent on travelling doctors, mostly quacks, and on district midwives. A licensing act of 1815 was superseded in 1818, by an act which set up a board of five examiners, still including Dr. Macaulay. By this time apprentices were being trained by the resident naval and military surgeons, both active and retired on half-pay. The Medical Board of Upper Canada, meeting in York once every three months, examined the applicants, passed some as fit to practice and usually rejected an equal number as unfit without further training.

The Canadian medical training, an apprenticeship of four or five years, was a combination of assistance to physicians, observation and a little reading. The apprentices were taught to imitate their teachers in bleeding, lancing, blistering, 'physicking', and the practice of midwifery. Major surgery was limited mainly to amputations. The Medical Board later added the requirement of a year's hospital or equivalent practice to secure qualification. The 'equivalent' was a necessary provision since there were then, in Upper Canada, no hospitals, except the naval and military ones.

From the beginning of settlement in 1783 there was a military hospital in Kingston. One document noted that it was discontinued, for a time in 1790, so that the space might be used to store presents for the Indians. In 1791 another document noted that the building had already been used some three years as an Indian storehouse but, since only one end was occupied, it was considered 'well calculated for use as an Hospital'. It continued in operation and was used often enough to bring a formal complaint, in 1809, from forty-four Kingston men who presented a memorial to Governor Sir James Craig. They asked for the removal of the hospital, then used only by seamen, and suggested several possible locations for a new hospital outside the town.

It is not clear what, if any, action was taken on this Kingston petition. The outbreak of the War of 1812 increased the need for hospital accommodation for both sailors and soldiers, and the old hospital was certainly in use during the war. An Ordnance map of 1816 showed three other naval and military hospitals in the town: in the 'French' church, in a North Street house, and northwest of the artillery parade ground. Beyond the town on Point Frederick there was a hospital in what is now part of the Commandant's Quarters at the Royal Military College, and another on Point Henry, near the shore.

At this time there was no civilian hospital, and really no need for one, as those who could afford medical care would not go to a hospital. The few sick poor were cared for in their own homes or, by arrangement with a religious society, placed in a boarding house to be given some care. After the War of 1812–15, the economic condition of the civilians in Kingston, especially of the labouring man, changed drastically. In 1812 Kingston had a population of about 1,000; by 1816 it had grown to 2,250. Many of these were disbanded militia men whose families, having moved to Kingston during the war, preferred to stay in the bigger settlement. When the Rush-Bagot Convention of 1817 limited the naval force on the Great Lakes, the navy shipyards closed. The workers were soon absorbed by commercial ship building firms, but their health care was no longer the responsibility of the naval authorities.

As immigration increased, the number of sick poor became an immediate and pressing problem in both Lower and Upper Canada. Public-minded citizens began to organize charity work to cope with the growing welfare problem. In Montreal the Ladies Benevolent Society established, in 1817, a House of Recovery to assist destitute emigrants. ('Emigrant,' not 'immigrant,' was the official term in use during the 1800s.) That same year, Kingstonians who had been giving help privately to the needy, organized the Kingston Compassionate Society to provide for 'the relief of the sick poor in their homes and to forward destitute emigrants to their place of destination'. But it was not only newcomers who needed help; within six months, a meeting of the Society considered whether to give help also to an applicant who was not a *bona fide* emigrant. The private charity work, thus organized, may have increased efficiency but it did little to increase the funds available.

In March 1818, a letter to the editor of the *Kingston Chronicle* from 'S.B.' (Surgeon Boyd of H.M. Navy), calling for a better organized system of furnishing relief in extreme cases of disease and poverty, started the first public movement in Kingston towards central medical care for the poor. There was an immediate response. Surgeon Joseph Scott, after attacking Boyd for signing only initials, presented an even more far-reaching appeal. He wrote that the 'poor and infirm demand our particular attention; to inform their minds; to repress their vices; to assist their labours; to invigorate their activity; and to improve their comforts'. Surgeon McGee wrote urging support for the establishment of an infirmary and dispensary for the sick poor and suggesting that a town meeting be called. As a result, the Magistrates, through the Court of Quarter Sessions, applied to the Lieutenant Governor for help. An Order in Council, dated 9 September 1818, granted in trust to Thomas Markland, Allan Maclean, and the Rev. George Okill Stuart five lots in Kingston as the site for a hospital building and six acres near-by for the support of the hospital. The prompt response to their request faced the

Magistrates with a problem familiar to many of the settlers – plenty of land but no cash to enable them to make use of it. The Magistrates' decision on how to meet this problem required a period of deliberation.

Six months later, in February 1819, the Magistrates and inhabitants of the Midland District met at Bath. Their resolutions set forth three aims: the formation of a society for bettering the condition of the poor of the Midland District, the introduction of savings banks (evidently to make sure the number of poor did not increase), and the establishment of a hospital for the general use of the district. Later that month it was announced that shares at £2.10 each, were to be subscribed for in order to raise a fund for the hospital building which would be started as soon as two hundred shares were taken up. A subscribers' list began immediately.

Less than half the necessary shares, however, had been taken up by May, three months later. Then the government, discontinuing funds for maintenance of the poor, caused a crisis in relief work. Funds were urgently needed to support the new society for the poor, and provide additional help for the Compassionate Society. Appeals for relief funds, coupled with the sale of shares in the new Kingston bank, however, made it difficult to sell more shares in the hospital fund. The project was therefore in jeopardy. But hope was rekindled early in 1820 with the possibility that the Loyal and Patriotic Society of Upper Canada might make a grant to the fund; instead the grant was given to help the York Hospital building fund. The small fund of the Kingston branch of that Society was used to buy a church organ.

Meanwhile the Compassionate Society had remained active. On the second floor of Blockhouse No. 1 they had fitted up a room as a hospital 'to avoid the expence attending the board of sick persons'. Their temporary hospital closed as usual on the first of May in 1820; and before it was reopened in November there had been a reorganization of charitable work in Kingston. To help destitute emigrants the men formed a short-lived Emigrant Society; and the Female Benevolent Society took on the care of the sick poor, which had been the main work of the Compassionate Society.

The Ladies of the Female Benevolent Society, an ecumenical group, included women from the families whose names had appeared on the 1819 list of hospital fund shareholders. These families were to be involved for over a century in charitable work in Kingston. For more than twenty years the Female Benevolent Society provided the only hospital care for the sick poor in Kingston, first in old blockhouses and then in an empty brewery warehouse. Their hospital opened in November and closed the first of May, providing during the winter months, food, shelter, and minimal nursing care, which was usually more important than the medical care. Naval and military surgeons, many retired on half-pay, and the growing number of civilian doctors continued to give free medical care to the poor, both in and out of the Female Benevolent Society hospital.

The 1819 campaign for a hospital for the sick poor may have had some influence in the decision of certain medical men to settle in Kingston where six or seven doctors were already in practice. In August and September 1820, four surgeons advertised the opening of their practices to the inhabitants of Kingston and vicinity. Two of those four surgeons were to be of great importance in the founding of the Kingston General Hospital and in the programme of health care in the area.

Dr. Edmund W. Armstrong, born in Fredericksburg on the Bay of Quinte, was passed as qualified to practise medicine by the Medical Board of Upper Canada in July 1819, after his training at Dartmouth College in New Hampshire. He had practised at Hallowell before he came to Kingston in September 1820. Dr. Armstrong's Loyalist family connections gave him an immediate acceptance in the community and also assured him a reasonable practice.

The second doctor who was to have an even greater impact on medical care in Kingston, through both the Hospital and the medical school, was Dr. James Sampson. Born in Ireland in 1789, he was educated in Dublin and received his hospital training at the Middlesex Hospital and at the York Military Hospital at Chelsea. He joined the 85th Regiment of Foot in June 1811, and a year later he was in Canada where he served as Assistant Surgeon with the Newfoundland Fencibles during the War of 1812. In August 1815, he was transferred to the 104th Regiment of Foot and was retired on half-pay in July 1817, after the Regiment was disbanded in Montreal. He stayed first in Niagara, then briefly in Queenston, before he came to Kingston in September 1820.

Dr. Sampson had been stationed in Kingston with his regiment during the war. When he returned in 1820 he had letters of introduction to some of the important citizens of the town. It was, however, his wider acquaintance with politically important men in Upper Canada which gained for him a position of some importance in Kingston and in the Province. In August 1821, he was appointed a Magistrate of the Midland District and in April 1822, on the death of Dr. James Macaulay, he was appointed to the Medical Board of Upper Canada. Caring for the sick poor and improving the standard of medical care in Kingston and the district added to Dr. James Sampson's duties and responsibilities but added little to his income. His practice increased, especially among the poor who paid nothing, but also among the wealthy who paid their doctor's bills at their leisure. His name appeared year after year in the list of local doctors who gave free medical care at the request of the Female Benevolent Society. In 1828, in order to supplement his income for the support of his ailing wife and five daughters, he was impelled to apply for a recently vacant government post, Inspector of Licences, Midland District, a position he held from 1829 to 1849. He also had some medical students and was involved in the formation of the Midland District Medical Society.

missioners for the Hospital had to defer their plans for the future in order to deal with an immediate crisis involving the health of the town. On 14 June 1832, a public meeting resolved to adopt measures to prevent the spread of cholera. They agreed to clean up the town, cart away garbage and remove all pigs from the town within twenty-four hours. On June 17th the first death from cholera was reported in town and the yellow flag was raised on the market place near the harbour. All troops were confined to their barracks and their families were moved from town to a camp on Point Henry, by order of the commanding officer, to institute a tight quarantine.

The next day the Magistrates met in special session and decreed strict regulations for the duration of the epidemic. No boat was to enter the harbour until it had been inspected by the Health Officer; and any master who brought a sick or dead person to Kingston on his boat was to be fined. The carters of Kingston were ordered to hold themselves ready to take, on a doctor's order, any sick person to the hospital which the Magistrates would provide. They set up a Central Board of Health and accepted Dr. Evans's offer to take charge of the cholera hospital, which was established in a warehouse. Captain Lelievre, of the Royal Navy, was made Harbour Master and Dr. Thomas W. Robison, Health Officer. Every morning at ten, three members of the Board of Health – different men from day to day – were to meet to take any necessary action; leaving the medical men free to treat the sick. In spite of their precautions cholera came, and remained to run its course.

Calomel, castor oil with laudanum, bleeding, and various stimulants were used in attempts to treat the dread disease. Dr. Sampson, working with Staff Surgeon Walter Henry, tried, as a last resort, a transfusion of saline fluid into the veins of some bad cases. The first effect was almost miraculous but there was a later relapse and all twenty patients given that treatment died, as did many, many others.

Kingston's streets were almost empty, except for funeral carts, and business was at a standstill until the end of the epidemic in October. The troops and their families came out of quarantine and life gradually resumed its normal pace. The cholera hospital was closed and, in November, the Female Benevolent Society opened its hospital for the winter.

The Commissioners resumed work on the plans for the General Hospital with their local architect, Thomas Rogers. A Montreal friend wrote recommending changes in the heating system and water closets from those shown on the plans for the Montreal General Hospital. In the early spring of 1833, the Commissioners and Thomas Rogers, who was to be the superintending architect, went to Montreal to look over the building there. They met the hospital officials and the Montreal architect to have a final conference on the plans for the Kingston building. When they returned to Kingston tenders were called with a closing date of May 6th. On a memorandum of that date seven tenders were listed for the Commissioners to consider. The contract for masonry and brick work amounting to £1,525 went to John and Thomas Milner. John Fisher and William Lyall's tender for the carpenter work was accepted at £1,424 and a small painting contract went to James Kerr for £17.15.10. Contracts were signed in July 1833, calling for completion of the building by March 1835.

With contracts signed and work under way supervised by Thomas Rogers, the Commissioners, somewhat concerned, began to consider how the Hospital would be supported when it was open for the care of the sick poor. On 13 December 1833, they addressed a petition to Sir John Colborne, Lieutenant Governor of Upper Canada, soliciting an endowment for the Kingston General Hospital so as to assure adequate and continued support beyond the voluntary contributions they might expect. They were encouraged by a committee report to the House of Assembly, the next March, recommending that the Lieutenant Governor grant waste lands of the Crown for the support of both the Kingston and the York hospitals. The House of Assembly sent the recommendations to Sir John Colborne who sent them to London for final approval.

To make sure that the Kingston Hospital would get waste land, if it should become available, Dr. James Sampson, for the Commissioners, made formal application for a grant of Crown Lands, estimating the need of an income of £1,000 annually for the support of the Kingston Hospital. In asking for this grant he explained that the Hospital should be considered not as a local but rather as a provincial or national establishment since it would care for mariners and for emigrants. The government records showed that land had been granted to a Kingston hospital in 1819. But a minute of the Executive Council 3 July 1834, sent to Dr. Sampson, stated that those town lots were needed for the military and that an equivalent grant of land in the town should be made in their place. There is no record however of that equivalent grant. Two years later, the request for Crown waste lands was refused, with the notation that such grants could not be allowed to any single holder, institutional or otherwise.

That the Commissioners had time to write petitions in that summer of 1834 was surprising, for Kingston was in the midst of the worst cholera epidemic of its history. Over three hundred deaths were reported, including ten per cent of the men on the list of contributors to the Hospital fund. The *British Whig* said that the deaths reported to the Board of Health were very few compared to the actual mortality. A staff surgeon, writing about the 1834 epidemic, noted that there was a change in the treatment for cholera – not so much bleeding and less calomel and fewer stimulants. But the death list grew until cold weather brought relief.

An interesting advertisement appeared that summer of 1834, when the cholera epidemic was at its height. The Kingston, Montreal, and Quebec newspapers carried an announcement of a Medical Academy, under the immediate patronage of Sir John Colborne, to be opened in Kingston on August 1st. Mr. G. Colls, Surgeon, R.N., offered to instruct gentlemen in all branches of the medical profession. The terms were £100 per annum, including tuition, board, lodging and washing. But beyond the advertisement there is no record of such a school.

After such a tragic summer, when a hospital had been so badly needed, there came from the government, in November, a request for a report on the Kingston Hospital, asking several questions, which brought forth Dr. Sampson's wry sense of humour. In his report of December 1834 he wrote, in part, 'And first with respect to "the period during which it has existed" we beg to remark that the establishment which was the object of the address presented to His Majesty by the House of Assembly last session, and in which His Excellency has been pleased to take a warm and very gratifying interest, cannot yet be said to "exist".' To indicate the basis and need for the Kingston Hospital, the report gave a brief history of the Female Benevolent Society hospital, particularly of its financial support and of the 'class of persons' treated there. It concluded with the request for an endowment to give an annual sum of £1,000 for the support of the Hospital.

The completion date for the Hospital, March 1835, could not be met. Contractors had been delayed by lack of labourers, especially during the cholera epidemic. And, with two other major projects in the area – the new Provincial Penitentiary and the rebuilding of Fort Henry – competition for able workmen had been keen. But, in June 1835, the contracts for the Kingston Hospital were completed; Kingston had a hospital building near the town.

Two

Kingston attained its hospital building in 1835, twenty-six years after the first campaign for funds for that purpose. The story of the Kingston Hospital over the next decade is recorded briefly in the Commissioners' yearly reports to the govern- ment and is rounded out by documents and by stories in the local newspapers. And it is a story in which Dr. James Sampson plays an important role. The *Canada Herald* of 12 June 1835 said: 'The Kingston Hospital, which has been in the course of erection for almost two years, is now nearly completed. It presents a fine appearance. Eighty-nine feet four inches long fifty-three feet four inches wide, four stories high, rooms lofty and well ventilated; can accommodate about 120 patients. It has two fronts and is approached by a handsome flight of stone steps. Dr. Sampson is appointed physician to the Hospital.'

The *Herald* was only partly right – the contracts made in 1833 were completed and the extras on two contracts had been paid. Dr. Sampson's appointment as physician, however, was to the new Provincial Penitentiary a mile beyond the Hospital, not to the Kingston Hospital which was far from being ready for use – especially so, in terms of funds available. The inside had not been painted; no baths or water closets had been installed; and the building was completely devoid of furnishings of any kind. On the grounds a huge mound of earth impeded the approach to the building. By December 1835, after paying for just a priming coat of paint on the columns, outside doors and window frames, the Commissioners had a balance of only £1.14.10 and they still owed Thomas Rogers, the superintending architect, £18.16.11.

The Commissioners' report to the Lieutenant Governor, Sir Francis Bond Head, in February 1836, gave two reasons for such a small balance. First, they had to spend £540 to buy land as a site for the Hospital when they had hoped for a grant of public land. Second, the voluntary contributors' fund had an unpaid balance of over £172, which they were not likely to be able to collect because of deaths and 'other untoward circumstances'. The Commissioners expressed a hope that His Excellency would see fit to recommend to the Legislature a further grant of £500 to enable them to finish and to furnish the Kingston Hospital so that this public charity institution could become an asylum for the sick poor of the district.

They also cited a recent tragic occurrence which emphasized the immediate and urgent need for the Kingston Hospital to be put into operation. On 21 December 1835, the government building which the Female Benevolent Society had used as a hospital had been destroyed by fire, with the loss of one life and of all the material gathered so carefully over the years. What the Commissioners did not say was that the Female Benevolent Society was in equally dire financial straits. The Society's balance in November 1835 was only £6.4.7½ and their appeal to the public was not very successful.

The Commissioners' appeal to Sir Francis Bond Head was completely un-rewarding. The only response from the Government in 1836 was a letter to Dr. Sampson informing him that his request of two years before for a grant of waste lands of the Crown to support the Kingston General Hospital had been denied. Obviously no humbly expressed hope to the Lieutenant Governor was sufficient; a direct petition to the Legislature was necessary. Consequently, the clergy and inhabitants of Kingston, late that year, petitioned for a grant of £500 for the Hospital, mentioning the destruction of the Female Benevolent Society hospital and expressing the urgent need for a refuge for the sick poor.

A grant in aid of the Kingston Hospital was passed in March 1837, and work to finish the Hospital was started in June when the £500 arrived. But time and weather had taken their toll of the unoccupied building. Doors and windows had been damaged, drain pipes inside the building had frozen and burst so that the water closet arrangements had to be sacrificed. Furthermore, the estimates of two years before were no longer adequate for the complete cost of the painting and grounds work; but by early fall what could be paid for had been done. Now that the Kingston Hospital was progressing toward operation, the Commissioners hoped that it would be further supported by the Legislature and by the public.

The temper of the country, however, was not conducive to orderly progress. In Lower Canada there was ferment; in Upper Canada, beyond Kingston, there were growing rumbles of discontent. Kingstonians felt that their way of life was threatened and on 2 November 1837, at a public meeting they resolved 'to support with our lives and fortunes the supremacy of the British constitution and the just dependence of the Canadas on the British Crown'. Then rumour became fact. On 6 December 1837, an early stage from Toronto told of a rebel gathering; a later, express stage brought news that the rebels were about to attack. The citizens of Kingston feared that very soon they might have to put their resolutions into effect.

The Magistrates called the citizens together to organize the protection of the town. (Most of the regular troops from the Kingston garrison had left for Lower Canada.) The town was divided into wards and Magistrates headed the dusk-to-dawn patrols, with Dr. Sampson, the Chief Magistrate, in charge of the town. The Hospital building, being outside the town defences, was not included in the patrols. Within a week Kingston was teeming with men from the countryside who were formed into militia companies to take over the defence of the town under the command of Lt. Col. Richard Bonnycastle, commander of the Royal Engineers. The threat to the town, however, did not materialize and by Christmas many of the volunteers had gone home.

Dr. Sampson could then take time to write for the Lieutenant Governor the annual report of the Commissioners of the Kingston Hospital. Since one Commissioner, John Macaulay, had left Kingston for Toronto in October when he was appointed Surveyor General, only Dr. Sampson and Dr. Armstrong signed the 1837 report. It was factual, brief, and specific, explaining the use of the £500 grant. They reported that they had purchased eighteen cheap bedsteads and bedding, that a fire was kept burning constantly in a large stove in the basement to protect the Hospital from frost and damp, and that more supplies were necessary to prepare the Hospital for the actual reception of patients. The report concluded 'and they take this opportunity to state to Your Excellency, that they are not aware that any provision has yet been made to meet the expenses, which must unavoidably be increased in order to carry the benevolent intention of the Legislature, and private donors, into effective operation, and that without such provision the building must necessarily remain useless and the just expectations of the public disappointed, all of which is most respectfully submitted.'

The lack of adequate government support for the maintenance of this charity hospital was to be the *leit motif* of the reports for a great many years. However, during the next few years, 1838 to 1844, the government took a more positive interest in the building – but not for use as a hospital. Actually the government was interested in any building, preferably in town, which would provide adequate shelter for the militia when they were called to active duty. In February 1838, when the militia was recalled to meet an expected invasion from American sympathizers, the Commissioners offered the Hospital building for use as a barracks and it may have been used as such for a short time. Lt. Col. Bonnycastle, writing to the Ordnance early in April, suggested that the building should be used as a military hospital and that the old military hospital in town be converted to a barrack.

The rebellion troubles deprived the Hospital of a Commissioner when Dr. E. W.

Armstrong, believing that he would be happier south of the border, moved to Rochester. Dr. James Sampson, the one Commissioner still in Kingston, having turned the Hospital over to the military authorities, had a few months of more normal activity before the next invasion scare. He again accepted an appointment to the Medical Board of Upper Canada, under a new commission from Sir George Arthur; and he viewed with approval the new town council's by-law setting up a Board of Health.

When trouble flared again, the militia was recalled. On 1 November 1838, Kingston established a night watch with Dr. Sampson as Captain Commandant of the Town Guard. Within a few days the militia had again taken over and Dr. Sampson, commissioned a Major in the 3rd Frontenac Militia, was ordered to six months' duty on Wolfe Island, a vulnerable point in the possible invasion route. The town was crowded with militia even after many were sent down river to the battle scene.

That November, after the Battle of the Windmill near Cornwall, the Kingston Hospital was used for the first time as a hospital to house wounded American prisoners. Twenty men were sent to the Hospital; two died of their wounds. Some of them were still in the Hospital, early in January 1839, when the Militia Court Martial suspended its sittings. Major James Sampson had been a member of that Court Martial, sitting with it from November 26th through December.

By early spring normal life had been resumed in Kingston and the sick poor became once again the responsibility of the town. After the sick prisoners had been removed from the Hospital, Dr. Sampson, informed that the building was no longer needed by the government, inspected it for possible damage. He sent off at once a list of repairs needed to restore the building to its former state, repairs which should be made before the government relinquished control. There seems to have been no immediate reply. In June 1839, Dr. Sampson asked for assurance that if the Commissioners took possession of the Hospital it would not invalidate their request for repairs. He was assured that it would not, that the government was anxious for him to take possession, and that the repairs would be made. But it was November before the Commissariat called for tenders for the repair of 'the Hospital near Stuart's Point'.

Commissioner Sampson had, meanwhile, become Mayor Sampson after the sudden death of Mayor Henry Cassidy in September 1839. Consequently he had pressing problems beyond the empty Hospital building. The new Governor General, Charles Poulett Thomson (later Lord Sydenham), visited Kingston, and the citizens' address, presented by the Mayor, put forth the proposal that if there were to be a union of the two provinces, Kingston be made the capital city.

Other things were happening in Upper Canada which affected the future of the Hospital. Dr. Sampson was appointed one of the three commissioners to arrange for the erection of a lunatic asylum in the province. He was painfully aware that there was a desperate need for such an institution for there were inmates under his care in the Provincial Penitentiary who were mental cases, not criminals. The other two commissioners were from Toronto and voted to place the first lunatic asylum in that city.

The ladies who had been members of the Female Benevolent Society, dormant since 1836, called a meeting to resurrect the Society. On reorganization it assumed a different form and set as its main object the promotion of industry among the poor, with emphasis on 'the awful evils of intemperance'. There was still no hospital for the sick poor.

A movement that was to have a long-time effect on the Kingston Hospital had now begun within the Presbyterian community in Kingston. In the fall of 1839, while one committee of the church was composing a petition to the Legislature to establish a college in Kingston, another committee was looking for temporary accommodation for the college. They met with Dr. Sampson to consider the Hospital building, which, now repaired but still lacking operating funds, would deteriorate if not in some kind of use. Dr. Sampson as Commissioner, and the Rev. Dr. John Machar and John Mowat, as contributors to the Hospital fund, petitioned the Legislature to allow the temporary occupation of the Hospital by the proposed university. An Act authorizing the lease, 'for such term of years and such annual rent as His Excellency, the Lieutenant Governor, would deem proper', was passed in February 1840.

Commissioners John Macaulay and James Sampson, as directed, set the terms of the lease which was brought before the Queen's College Trustees in May. Before this meeting, Mayor Sampson, re-elected late in March, had other problems which seriously affected the economy of the town. A disastrous fire swept the water front in Kingston in April with a loss of almost £90,000. The immediate problem was to control the rebuilding of the burned area to prevent fire hazards as much as possible and to improve the commercial district. During May the Town Council was busy drafting fire control by-laws; but eventually the real control was effected by the insurance companies who refused to write policies for wooden buildings in the down town area. This affected the supply of cheap accommodation near the wharves for transients and emigrants. Businessmen found that the new regulations steeply raised the cost of rebuilding.

The Queen's College Trustees, after serious consideration, at their May 22nd meeting, resolved to decline the offer of the lease of the Hospital. They felt that three years at £150 a year was not only too short a lease at too great a cost, but that the necessary alterations to the building would have been expensive. So, that summer the Hospital building was again a problem for Commissioner Sampson, as the usual flow of destitute emigrants into the town was a problem for Mayor

Sampson. At the height of the season, when all other available accommodation was full, a few emigrants were housed temporarily in the Hospital.

Dr. Sampson, as Mayor, was fully aware of the value of a large, empty building in the possible future of Kingston. He knew that Kingston was under serious consideration by the Governor General as the capital of the United Provinces of Upper and Lower Canada. He even had secret information of its selection some time before the newspapers began publishing rumours about it. The Governor General, who had become Lord Sydenham when the Union Bill received Royal Assent in July 1840, had decided on Kingston as early as September 1840. The next month he negotiated privately, through Dr. Sampson and others, the purchase of land which he intended should be the site of permanent Parliament Buildings (the present City Park). The Kingston Hospital building was selected to be the temporary Parliament Building. Offices, however, would be on Ontario Street in the new Marine Railway offices. Dr. Sampson helped to arrange the lease of Alwington House, the home of Charles W. Grant, Baron de Longueuil, to be the official residence of the Governor General. (The house was destroyed by fire in 1958.)

The selection of Kingston buildings for the temporary accommodation of the government was made before the newspapers could do more than speculate on the activities of the various government officials then visiting in Kingston. The choice of Kingston as the capital was not officially announced until 15 February 1841, when the Union was proclaimed and Parliament was called to meet in Kingston in June.

The Hospital Commissioners had a tenant; the agreed price of £300 a year for the temporary use of the building was to be paid in the form of an annual grant for the support of the indigent sick in Kingston. A week before the official announcement was made, the Hospital building and grounds began to undergo alterations recommended by the government architect, George Browne of Montreal, and hurriedly approved by the Governor General. The grounds were cleaned up, a well dug, a privy and wood shed built, and a long shed erected for the horses and the carriages of the Members. A turnstile and entrance gate opened onto the new board walk and avenue leading to the south entrance to the Hospital.

The architect's statement of expenditures and the painting contract, in documents in the Public Archives of Canada, give details of the changes made in the Hospital building. Some partitions were removed to provide two rooms each 47 x 22 x 12 feet. They were used for the House of Assembly (84 members) and for the Legislative Council (24 members) and each had a Speaker's platform and a reporter's box with stairs. The railing in the Council Room was black walnut, the benches painted red; in the House the railing and the benches were green. Rooms for the Governor General, the President and the Clerk of Council had the walls distempered, the woodwork painted white, and the doors grained and varnished. Rooms for the Speaker and the Clerk of Assembly were similarly decorated. A library was fitted up and two new rooms were made in the attic storey by putting semicircular windows in each of the four gables. When the government furniture arrived from Toronto the building which had been erected for the care of sick indigents took on, especially in the Governor General's room, the trappings of viceroyalty.

Buildings went up all over Kingston and on the Front Road near the Hospital – houses for government officials and new commercial buildings. The economy boomed. In April 1841, John Counter became Mayor of Kingston and Dr. Sampson then devoted himself to his large and growing practice, which included consultation with Dr. James Farnden, Assistant Surgeon of the 70th Regiment, on the health of the Governor General. Dr Sampson was said to be one of few Kingstonians who was a frequent guest at Lord Sydenham's private dinner table at Alwington House that summer of 1841.

For the next three years the story of the Kingston Hospital is the story of the political health of the new Union of the Provinces. Although the basis for Canadian government was laid within its walls and new laws were born in its refurbished wards, old antipathies were unfortunately revived and jealousies strengthened. Political fortunes were made and lost and three Governors General occupied the Governor's Room.

Lord Sydenham in the blue and silver dress uniform of the Governor General, escorted from Alwington House by a detachment of the King's Dragoon Guards, arrived at the Parliament Buildings in Kingston, on 15 June 1841, to read the speech from the throne. On September 25th he was carried from Alwington House in a funeral procession, past the Parliament Buildings, to his grave in a vault beneath the main aisle of St. George's Cathedral, the victim of lockjaw from injuries suffered in a fall from his horse.

The new Governor General, Sir Charles Bagot, arrived in January 1842 to find among many other problems, growing agitation for the removal of the seat of government from Kingston. But Bagot was mortally ill and even before he died, in Alwington House, Sir Charles Metcalfe had to take over as the third Governor General. He was easily convinced that Kingston as the capital was acceptable to no one but Kingstonians. On 3 November 1843, the measure was passed which moved the capital to Montreal. When the Governor General left in July 1844, only two government departments remained in Kingston – the office of the Adjutant of Militia and the Emigrant Office. Kingston's new Municipal Building was now finished, and the Hospital building was again empty.

During the years that Kingston was the capital there was little unemployment. Every man who could work was employed in the building trades and women were in great demand as domestic help in the Members' homes and in the many boarding houses. Consequently, the Female Benevolent Society had little need to provide work for the poor and there were very few indigent sick in Kingston. But the emigrant problem was more serious than ever with no available accommodation of any kind, even for the sick. The Ladies of the Female Benevolent Society, therefore, returned to their hospital work.

They again used one of the old blockhouses as their emigrant hospital. In August 1841, when they were informed that the army needed it for accommodation for the women of the regiment, they protested vehemently that their patients had no place else to go. The Ladies were allowed to use the blockhouse only to the end of that emigrant season. Their usual winter hospital did not open until December 13th that year. They found accommodation in premises leased from James Morton, the distiller, which had once before been used as a temporary emigrant hospital. The records of their hospital work for this period are meagre as the problem of health care was greatly overshadowed by public affairs and the booming economy.

The political manoeuvring which moved the capital to Montreal brought depression to Kingston. With the next session of Parliament scheduled for Montreal, Members left town early in the year and more and more houses became empty, and more taxes were unpaid. Dr. Sampson was again elected Mayor, since John Counter had moved outside the town limits to his country estate (the present Sunnyside Children's Home). Dr. Sampson took office in April 1844, to preside over a town with a heavy debt for its new Municipal Building, with many businessmen hard-pressed if not bankrupt, and with widespread unemployment.

In June the Governor General left Kingston. The Mayor escorted Sir Charles Metcalfe to the wharf, saw him aboard his ship, and returned to the troubles and trials of the municipality. It was not a happy situation: the Town Council was accused by many citizens of inefficiency and, by some, of shady financial deals. Tempers flared in Council over the appointment of some Catholics as special constables for the Orange parade on July 12th. Mayor Sampson, in disgust, handed in his resignation to take effect as soon as his successor was elected by the Council. By September Dr. Thomas W. Robison was Mayor and Dr. Sampson could happily attend to his duties as Commissioner of the Kingston Hospital.

Alterations to the building to make it suitable for Parliament now needed to be changed again to fit it for a hospital. However, the government was still officially in possession and, being immediately concerned with getting settled in Montreal, ignored the requests that control of the building be returned to the town. Dr. Sampson felt that immediate action was called for; with unemployment at a high level there was need for more accommodation for the indigent sick. Getting any kind of action from a government pleased to be out of Kingston seemed to be impossible. In March 1845, Dr. Sampson sent to Secretary Daly a claim regarding the cost of reconditioning the Hospital. There evidently was no reply – or at least no satisfactory reply – because the editor of the *Upper Canada Herald*, in May, asked how the people might deal with this problem. 'Are they to go and take forcible possession of the building? As the Government has robbed them, are they in return to rob the Government?'

Repeated applications to the government to settle the problem of legal control of the building were not satisfactorily answered until 1847. But, by the early fall of 1845, some assurance was given that the building might be used as a hospital. The Commissioners made the arrangements and the Ladies of the Female Benevolent Society appealed successfully for funds and furnishings. Consequently, the *Kingston Chronicle and Gazette* of 12 November 1845, carried the following notice:

The Hospital for the use of the town of Kingston, under the superintendence of the Ladies of the Female Benevolent Society, is open in the building lately occupied by the Provincial Parliament and patients will, on the certificate of a medical man that they are proper recipients for public charity, be admitted on the order of one of the following ladies who have consented to act as Directresses of the Society.

Mrs. Harper	*Mrs. de Blanquière*
Mrs. Askew	*Mrs. Williamson*

VISITORS

Mrs. R. D. Cartwright	*Mrs. A. McLean*
Mrs. Rogers	*Mrs. Strange*
Miss Wilkinson	*Mrs. Machar*
Mrs. S. Kirkpatrick	*Mrs. McGibbon*
Mrs. Dupuy	*Miss McDonald*
Mrs. Herchmer	*Miss Woodburne*
Mrs. Muccleston	*Miss Fowler*
Mrs. Watkins	*Mrs. Robison*
Mrs. Deykes	*Mrs. Henderson*
Miss Harper	*Mrs. Radcliffe*
Mrs. Williams	*Miss Dike*

Mrs. Corbett

Medical Man during the month of November Dr. Robison.
Applicants requiring medical advice and medicine only to attend at the Hospital at 11 o'clock A.M.

Three

The Kingston Hospital building, finished in 1835, was opened as a charity hospital *Female* in 1845. At that time Kingston, with a population of about 8,000, was petitioning *Benevolent* for incorporation as a city and hoping to annex the five farm lots to the west of the *Society* town limits (then at West Street) as far as Alwington House, next to the Provincial *Relinquishes* Penitentiary. Residents of those farm lots, especially of Farm Lot 24 which included *Control* the Kingston Hospital, opposed the annexation with such vigour that the Kingston *1846–1866* Incorporation Bill of 1846 annexed only Farm Lot 25, the present City Park. Four years later, when the Municipal Bill was passed, the other farm lots became part of the city and the Kingston Hospital was then in, not merely near, the city.

Kingston's disappointment in not getting the first lunatic asylum, which went to Toronto, was offset by the announcement of plans for extensive military building in and around the city. Once again the value of being a garrison town was evident as the Market Battery took shape in front of the City Hall and the Martello Towers were built on the perimeter of the city. Labourers found work while many property owners still had empty buildings and could not pay their taxes.

There were problems, beyond financial ones, which were plaguing all municipalities. Two of the most critical ones, from the standpoint of public health, were the supply of pure water and the disposal of waste. The first Kingston sewer was installed in the early 1830s and extended in 1837 but it serviced only a small part of the town. Most of the households had privies, ranging from simple pits to small outhouses referred to as 'the usual offices'. Sewage from these was hauled away by the 'night soil' carters and not hauled very far away; in Kingston, in the winter, it was dumped on the river or lake ice all too near the shore. Supplies of slaked lime were provided free for use in privy pits, but only during epidemics, to encourage the poor to take sanitary precautions. There was very questionable drainage for the cesspools dug in the limestone, often near wells. Water, for those without wells, was delivered in puncheons which the carters filled from the lake along the Front Road. If the water looked clean and was free from odour it was presumed to be fit to drink.

The then current ideas on preventive medicine emphasized proper ventilation, since it was thought that infection came from 'noxious effluvia'. The Kingston Hospital, it was noted in a local paper, was 'well ventilated'. Yet Queen's College, in 1853, considering the purchase of Summerhill House just opposite the Hospital, was afraid that disease might be blown their way. The Trustees consulted the doctors for assurance that the large house, built on a rise and open to the fresh lake breezes, was out of danger to students from effluvia.

The disease and death rate, especially of children, among the poor was very high; and, even among the well-to-do, the incidence of respiratory and contagious diseases was alarming. Disease was generally associated with noxious vapours, toxic substances, infections, and parasitic agents. Treatment, for the most part, was limited to bleeding, sweating, and doses of physic, diuretics, and emetics to purge the patient. The basic kit for a doctor had plenty of calomel, a cupping set to raise blisters and a scarifier with a series of small blades to induce bleeding.

To quote Bernard J. Stern in *Society and Medical Progress* (1941): '*The Cyclopaedia of Practical Medicine*, published in 1845, advised that the amount of bloodletting depended upon the heart and pulse, but in most cases should be between ten and fourteen ounces, while apoplexy required the loss of from forty to fifty ounces. Samuel Gross reports the usual amount to have been sixteen to twenty-four ounces, and states that patients felt cheated if less was extracted.'

In 1845 there were about a dozen doctors in Kingston, besides the few navy and army surgeons, attached to units stationed in or near the city, some of whom had no private practice. Most of the local doctors had received their training in British or American hospitals or medical schools and they had all been declared qualified by the government Medical Board, of which Dr. Sampson was a member. Formal medical training in Canada West was just beginning in the medical school at King's College, Toronto, which had been opened in January 1844. But local doctors had their private students in an apprentice arrangement.

Kingston, in the fall of 1845, had two civilian charity hospitals. The Sisters of Hotel Dieu had bought a stone building on Brock Street, near Regiopolis College (the present Hotel Dieu), and in September 1845, announced that it was open for the reception of patients. The Visiting Medical Officer was Dr. Hallowell, the Consulting Medical Officer, Dr. James Sampson.

Dr. Sampson was in a peculiar position so far as the Kingston Hospital was concerned. He and John Macaulay, who had returned to Kingston, as Commissioners under the original Act were – so far as they could determine from the government – still solely responsible for the Hospital building. They had no funds and no authority to operate it as a hospital but they could rent it to someone else. Consequently, in October 1845, the Commissioners granted the use of the Hospital building to the Ladies of the Female Benevolent Society to house their charity hospital.

The Society had raised about £200, which provided furnishings and supplies to fit up two wards. They then continued their pleas for more donations of food and bedding. A Mrs. Martin was hired as Housekeeper–nurse and her daughter as a helper. Nursing then was little more than maid service and these two women were to cook the meals, do the washing and keep the Hospital clean. Local doctors agreed to accept the medical responsibility and, in rotation, were in charge for a month at a time, offering their services free. Medical Officer for that first November was Dr. T. W. Robison; Dr. Horatio Yates, newly qualified, followed him. The general management was in the hands of the Directresses of the Female Benevolent Society and the volunteer visitors of that Society checked on the day to day operation of this charity Hospital.

According to the Society's plans their Hospital was to be, as before, a winter operation, closing as usual on the first of May. But when May 1846 came their two wards were full, the patients had nowhere else to go and more patients were waiting to be admitted. A hospital was needed all year; but after that first, very busy winter the Ladies decided that this was more than they could manage, both financially and in time and energy. The doctors agreed that the Hospital could no longer be properly run by volunteers or properly supported merely by donations. There had also been some criticism of the regulation and superintendence of the Hospital with the constant changes of those in charge, both doctors and visiting ladies.

In July 1846, a meeting was held in City Hall to present to the general public the problems of the management of the Hospital. The Ladies' case was presented. Some eighty-two patients had been treated since the Hospital was opened the previous November and with more patients admitted in May, the Hospital needed to be kept open all summer. There was, consequently, a need to establish a General Hospital which would be supported by a government grant, and a need to decide on the regulation and supervision of such a Hospital. The meeting resolved to apply for an act of Parliament to provide for the proper management. But the biggest problem was, of course, the financial support for the operation of the Hospital. A government continuing grant was the ideal solution. In case it could not be secured other sources of funds had to be considered. One suggestion was that a special ward for sailors might be established to be supported by subscriptions from ship owners.

Before an appeal could be made to the government for assistance certain legal details had to be settled. In August, the two Hospital Commissioners applied to the government to make sure that the trusteeship and control of the building was still vested in them. The answer, reassuring them, did not come until a year later. Meanwhile, another winter was approaching and, if the Hospital was to remain open, help was needed, not promises.

In November 1846, the Ladies of the Female Benevolent Society invited the public to a meeting at the Hospital to call their attention to the affairs of the Hospital. They hoped that the meagre furnishings of the two wards, with the other rooms completely empty, would emphasize their need for help. Once again they asked for an appeal to the government for an act of incorporation, to ensure a properly constituted board of management and to provide sufficient funds. This time action was taken; a committee was formed to draft an application to the government. And, in the meantime, a group of men offered to assist the Ladies and the doctors in the management of the Hospital until the government would take some action.

The campaign for incorporation ran into one difficulty after another. The Governor in Council recommended incorporation but the stumbling block was the part of the proposed act which set up an endowment to support the Hospital. The Legislature could not agree on the source of such an endowment and the act failed to pass.

Meanwhile Kingston was struck by another disastrous epidemic – typhus – when the emigration season opened in June 1847. The Board of Health took the usual precautions but was soon overwhelmed by the size of the problem. Thousands of Irish emigrants came to Kingston, many of them sick and dying. The Hospital and the Hotel Dieu were soon full and sheds had to be erected on Emily Street, on the government land near Murney Tower, to shelter more sick. Their families huddled on the board walk along the edge of the present City Park and begged for food. The welfare problem was almost as bad as the medical problem and still the emigrants continued to be dumped on the wharves at Kingston. A shed was built next to the Kingston Hospital, and when the Emily Street sheds were torn down on a court order, as being a public nuisance, another shelter was built on government land at the foot of the present Lower Albert Street. Most of the sick died and many who cared for them were victims also. Mrs. Martin and her daughter both died but volunteers carried on their work at the Hospital. The emigrant dead were buried in a huge trench near the Kingston Hospital and a great mound marked their common grave.

Kingston citizens were up in arms about the number of sick emigrants landed in Kingston, spreading disease to Kingstonians too. Death carts were a daily mournful sight throughout the summer as Kingston families were decimated. The Board of

Health suggested that a quarantine station might be set up on Garden Island or in the Naval Dockyard, but to no avail. They were horrified when, just as the epidemic was subsiding, the government announced that it would close all small emigrant hospitals within sixty miles and send the remaining patients to Kingston. Kingston had widows, orphans, and indigent persons to be cared for in their own population as well as in the emigrant sheds.

The petitions for incorporation of the Kingston Hospital continued to be ignored, though other institutions near Kingston were not ignored by the government. In 1848, the direction and management of the Provincial Penitentiary were investigated by a Parliamentary Committee on the demand of Dr. Sampson, who was surgeon to the institution. In a dispute over a matter of discipline Dr. Sampson's name had been mentioned and, although no charge of any sort had been made, he considered he had been maligned. He resigned and demanded that an inquiry be made into the dispute and the complete management of the Penitentiary. The resultant rumours, recriminations, and committee hearings occupied the attention of the people of Kingston throughout the summer and fall of 1848. The Warden and some other officials were forced to resign and were replaced before the hearings ended. The Committee report, tabled the next year in Parliament, revealed barbarities in the treatment of prisoners, and corruption and inefficiency in management. It completely exonerated Dr. Sampson who was asked to resume his post as Surgeon to the Penitentiary.

Meanwhile, the temporary management of the Hospital continued, with a committee of men assisting the Ladies of the Female Benevolent Society. Early in 1849, Mayor Francis M. Hill went to Montreal to ask Kingston's Member of Parliament, John A. Macdonald, to press for passage of a bill to incorporate the Kingston General Hospital. The bill, presented in March, received assent on 30 May 1849. Wording of the Act seems to indicate the approach which secured its passage as a national rather than a local project – 'to supply necessities and relieve the condition of sick and destitute Emigrants and other transients and the mariners of the Lakes . . .' The Act directed that the Commissioners be relieved of their charge and that a Corporation be established to manage and regulate the Hospital. This Corporation was to consist of the Mayor of Kingston; the Judge, the Warden, and the Sheriff, all of the Midland District; and three Aldermen elected by the City Council to serve as Trustees of the Hospital. The Act did not, however, make specific endowment arrangements for the continuing support of the Kingston Hospital, saying merely, 'a portion of the Marriage License Fund which may be appropriated by the Governor to the said Hospital and such other funds as might be received' should be managed by the Board of Governors of the Hospital.

At the first formal meeting of the Board of Governors, held 5 June 1849, the new trustees requested the title deeds for the land and a statement of affairs from the Commissioners. John Macaulay and James Sampson, who for seventeen years had been in charge, first of getting the building erected, then of keeping it in condition, now lost no time in giving up possession to the new trustees. Dr. Sampson handed over the title deeds and a sum of £40 to pay for repairs not yet complete. In a less formal way, the volunteer committee of men, the Female Benevolent Society, and the local doctors also handed over their responsibility for the charity Hospital. The officials took over from the volunteers. The doctors returned to personal charity work with their regular practice. The Ladies who had devoted their efforts for so many years to the care of the sick poor, turned to the care of widows and orphans.

When the Board of Governors took control of the Kingston General Hospital they had a good stone building, in need of some minor repairs, and a small amount of equipment, including fifty beds, with a total value of approximately £5,500. There were no other assets beyond the £40 for repairs turned over to them by Dr. Sampson. The only income, beyond possible donations, seems to have been the annual government grant of £300 for the care of emigrants. An additional £300 was granted to them in 1850.

According to the Minute Book of the Board of Governors there was no meeting, after that of 5 June 1849, until October 21st, when approval was given to arrangements made during the summer. William Young's appointment as Steward at a salary of £3 a month was confirmed. He and his family were allowed to occupy part of the basement until the space was otherwise required. General management of the Hospital was his responsibility. Dr. John A. Harvey, who had been qualified by the government Medical Board in April 1847, was appointed Surgeon to the Hospital at £50 a year to take care of the medical needs of the patients. There seems to have been no arrangement with the local doctors for any regular visiting, supervision, or consultation. This was to be a source of trouble. Men who had given their time and services free for years were ignored by the new Board, not out of pique but largely out of indifference or ignorance.

Entries in the Minute Book of this first Board of Governors are remarkably sparse for the first few years. They note appointments, with salary and living arrangements, contracts for rations, and also for straw for the patients' beds. The Governors signed a contract with John Wiley to provide rations for the patients at the rate of sixpence halfpenny per diet. According to the visitors' reports this provided dark bread and poor stewing beef. William Robinson succeeded William Young as Steward in July 1851, at the same rate of pay, £36 a year, but with a ration for himself only and the use of only two rooms in the basement. Two years later his pay was raised to £50 a year and Dr. Harvey received an increase to £100 a year as Surgeon.

Patients were admitted as before on an admission order signed by a member of the Board of Governors stating that they were legitimate recipients of charity. But there seems to have been no specific policy on what constituted indigency and no rules regarding the operation of the Hospital. Consequently there were soon charges and counter-charges of political preferment in the admission of cases, of inequity in the dismissal of patients, of gross inefficiency in management, and general lack of care for the building and grounds. Without the watchful eyes of the Ladies of the Female Benevolent Society, who had reorganized as the Widows' and Orphans' Friends Society to devote their energy and funds to that cause, and without the daily visits of the men's volunteer committee, the Hospital suffered. The Board of Governors left the management of the Hospital in the hands of the Steward and the Surgeon, although two members were supposed to visit the Hospital each week.

To be fair to the Governors, it must be said that they faced bigger problems in their other jobs than in the care of the sick poor, who, for all they knew, were adequately cared for at the Hospital. In this period the St. Lawrence Canals were opened and threatened the traditional role of Kingston as a transshipment point. The shipyards attempted to meet demands for new and different vessels and the forwarders looked for new kinds of business. Kingston was to be further threatened by the new railroads unless ways could be found to make them serve the interests of the city. The health of Kingston's commercial and industrial life depended on the energy of her politicians and the involvement of her wealthy men in the progress of the city and surrounding area. The health of the poor was another matter. The City Council presumed that the Board of Governors was doing its job, but the Board knew little, if anything, about hospital work and for the most part cared less.

Doctors were alienated by the lack of interest and the penury of the Board, discouraged by the mismanagement, and frustrated by the lack of organization at the Hospital. They carried on charity medical services from their own homes and offices, assisted in the care of the widows and orphans at the House of Industry and in various church charities. Besides that, they all had busy private practices. Dr. James Sampson, who continued to have a special interest in the affairs of the Kingston General Hospital, was also Surgeon to the Penitentiary and at this time deeply concerned with family illness. His wife died in February 1854, his third daughter a few weeks later.

Dr. Horatio Yates, returning to Kingston in 1853, after an illness, was shocked at the state of the Hospital and at the state of the management. He resolved that something must be done about the situation. Under the Act of Incorporation there was only one approach – through the Board of Governors – but the few who would listen did nothing. He decided that the old saw 'if you can't lick 'em, join 'em', was relevant to this problem. Consequently, Dr. Horatio Yates, aged thirty-one, who had studied with Dr. Sampson and trained in Philadelphia, and in London, persuaded Dr. John Robinson Dickson, aged thirty-three, to join him in running for a seat on City Council.

They were both elected, taking their seats in January 1854; both were named to the Board of Governors of the Kingston General Hospital. Dr. Yates was also elected Chairman of the Board of Health. A survey of the situation at the Hospital began in earnest. William Coverdale, architect, was asked to report on the physical state of the building and to recommend essential repairs. When the financial situation was reviewed the debt was found to be £736 and the yearly income only £600.

The non-medical members of the Board proposed that the Hospital be closed until the debt was paid; but Doctors Yates and Dickson urged them to keep the Hospital open. The doctors pointed out that the government grants were for the care of patients and would probably cease if the Hospital closed, even temporarily. Although there were fewer than twenty patients in the two wards, sick people could not be turned out and others would be needing hospital care. The Board agreed to keep the Hospital open if Dr. Yates would accept the primary responsibility.

Dr. Yates, given the opportunity to use his own ideas to improve the operation of the Hospital, then set to work. A new Steward was hired; controls were put on spending and every possible source of income was explored. Local doctors, hopeful that under Dr. Yates's energetic reorganization the Hospital would improve, gave money to meet immediate expenses. Board members pledged their personal credit to merchants for supplies while appeals went out for gifts of food and bedding. In the spring the Hospital grounds were ploughed so that potatoes could be planted. Dr. Yates, in his campaign for funds, talked to the builders of the Grand Trunk Railroad, offering to provide hospital care for their sick or injured workers for two shillings sixpence a day.

With the emigrant season approaching, Dr. Yates dealt with the health problem from two angles, prevention, and proper care. While he was supervising the clean-up and reorganization of the Hospital he was also doing his job as Chairman of the Board of Health. In a series of articles in the *Kingston Chronicle and News*, he urged the people of Kingston to clean up their homes and grounds, to keep animals off the streets, to improve drainage and to give themselves proper care so that they might avoid disease. He recommended that people should, if possible, sleep on the second or third floors of their homes to avoid noxious gases, stating that 'the malarious poison is of greater gravity than pure air, and hence its confinement to the lower strata of the aerial fluid (it being mixed with and suspended in the latter).'

The Hospital stayed open and the emigrant season of 1854 brought another cholera epidemic. But Kingston was better prepared than in previous epidemics. The Board of Health was well organized; no temporary cholera hospital was needed. The City Council, only too pleased to have a place to put the sick emigrants, advanced £150 for extra help at the hospital. By the middle of August there had been 130 deaths from cholera in Kingston. A news item gave the statistics for one day: 'August 6th: – interments 13, being citizens 7, Barriefield 2, strangers 4.' Kingston's preventive measures had helped, however, as the mortality rate in other centres was far higher.

The reorganization of the Hospital management and operation continued, with several important decisions concerning the medical responsibility made at a Board of Governors meeting late in August. Dr. Harvey, who was considered by Dr. Yates to be too inexperienced to be in sole charge, was appointed as Resident House Surgeon. He was to be constantly available, but to work henceforth under the supervision of the consulting and visiting surgeons. Formal invitations went from the Board to Dr. James Sampson to be Consulting Surgeon, and to Doctors John Mair, J. R. Dickson, O. S. Strange and Horatio Yates to be Visiting Surgeons. Dr. Harvey, unhappy with this new arrangement, resigned to be succeeded by Dr. Thomas Benson. A Matron and two male orderlies to work with the Steward completed the staff at the Hospital.

The public image of the Kingston General Hospital had improved since responsible people were in control and the Hospital began once again to receive the support of the charity-minded. A public meeting in December 1854 organized a drive for funds. Miss White's School for Young Ladies held a bazaar and raised £70 for the Hospital, and general donations increased. The Widows' and Orphans' Friends Society agreed to furnish a room and pay for the heating of it for the use of sick children from the House of Industry.

The management was reorganized, the chain of command clearly established, credit was improved but the debt remained. Extra economies had to be made and more money found. Some improvements had to be planned and it was clear that dependence on voluntary contributions was too uncertain, even for ordinary expenses. The Board asked for the advice of Kingston's member, John A. Macdonald, who sponsored an application for an increased grant which brought the Hospital £1,000 in 1855. The Board's attention could then go to drafting an amendment to their Act of Incorporation. The two doctors on the Board wanted to make sure that the Board of Governors would always have a few members who were actively interested in the Hospital and who would have some knowledge of the care of the sick.

Meantime a movement had started in Kingston which was to have a continuing and increasing role in the operation of the Kingston General Hospital. Queen's College, expanding and outgrowing its quarters on William Street, was, in the summer of 1853, considering the purchase of Summerhill House, Archdeacon Stuart's 'castle' on a rise just north of the Hospital. They were also resolving to expand further by starting faculties of law and medicine as soon as possible. Actually, the size of Kingston, the capacity of the Hospital, and the number of qualified doctors in the area made an early opening of a medical faculty unlikely. There was provision for private medical study; some doctors had a few students and the Act of Incorporation of the Hospital provided that any medical student in Kingston could visit the wards and attend them on payment of a fee and under the regulations of the Board of Governors. Dr. Sampson's students and many others received their hospital practice at the Kingston General Hospital. But there was no degree-granting medical school in Kingston.

A decision taken in Toronto brought about a more rapid realization of the plan to establish a medical faculty at Queen's. A group of medical students, who had transferred to Trinity College after the closing of King's College Medical School, were told that they could not graduate unless they were to become *bona fide* members of the Church of England. They found this unacceptable. One of them, Robert Douglass who had graduated from Queen's, wrote to Queen's Trustee John Mowat, that he wished there were a medical school in Kingston where they could be free of such religious tests. It is not clear whether this letter came before or after the first committee meeting in Kingston; but the assurance of eight senior students undoubtedly influenced the final decision to start classes in medicine.

On 7 February 1854, at the Brock Street home of John A. Macdonald, a committee of Queen's College Trustees met with some Kingston doctors, invited by Dr. J. R. Dickson, to consider setting up a medical school. Two weeks later, all the doctors in Kingston met, asked Dr. Sampson to chair the meeting, and resolved that a medical faculty should be established immediately. They proposed a list of names for the teaching appointments and selected a committee to present their plans to Queen's College. In March, Doctors Sampson, Stewart, Dickson and Strange met with the Queen's Trustees and proposed their plan. The proposal was handed for study to a committee of the Trustees.

The Medical Board of Upper Canada met in Kingston the first week in April 1854, to examine prospective doctors and to certify those they found qualified to practise. After the examinations Dr. Sampson felt that the findings of the Medical Board further served to emphasize the need for a medical school and for adequate training in a proper hospital. Dr. Horatio Yates's reorganization of the Kingston General Hospital assumed even greater importance.

In August, the Executive Committee of the Board of Trustees of Queen's College recommended, 'That the Board should give power to the Executive Committee to appoint Lecturers in Medicine, on whose report the Senatus Academicus might confer Degrees, and whose emoluments should be derived from the fees of the Students, and any funds which might hereafter be obtained for the special endowment of a School of Medicine.' They further recommended that the Lecturers procure two rooms for lectures and one for Anatomy and spend £50 for apparatus; the total outlay to be not more than £250.

Thus, the first session of Queen's Faculty of Medicine was to be, so far as salaries were concerned, a private venture on the part of the staff. They rented rooms in the former military hospital on Princess Street and opened the first session on 5 November 1854. There were twenty-three students: of the nine final-year men, eight were transfers from Trinity; one was Octavius Yates, a younger brother of Dr. Horatio Yates. There were thirteen second-year students and one beginner, Michael Sullivan of Kingston. Nine young men received the degree of Doctor of Medicine from Queen's College in the spring of 1855.

In June 1855, Queen's Trustees put the stamp of approval on the experimental first year and formally established a Faculty of Medicine, renting them space in the east wing of Summerhill. Dr. James Sampson was appointed President of the Faculty; the other staff members were Dr. John Stewart, Dr. J. R. Dickson, Dr. Horatio Yates, Dr. Fife Fowler, and Dr. J. P. Litchfield. The appointments were not given unanimous approval by the Queen's Trustees, for Queen's had never before appointed professors who were not Presbyterian clergymen. There was the fear, too, that this new faculty might draw too heavily on Queen's small income. Consequently, it was stipulated that no portion of the funds of the College were to be used to support the Faculty of Medicine; they would have to depend on student fees and special grants. The first government grant to the new Medical Faculty was £1,000, a source of some envy to the Faculties of Arts and Theology.

The course of study set out for Queen's medical students had an immediate effect on the affairs of the Kingston General Hospital. Payment of six dollars for the course in Clinical Medicine and the same for that in Clinical Surgery entitled the student to a ticket for Hospital attendance. As twelve months of hospital practice were required for a degree, the senior students were given immediate access to the Hospital to fulfill their requirements.

Dr. Horatio Yates, for the Hospital, and Dr. Sampson, for the Faculty of Medicine, proposed that the senior students, under the close supervision of their teachers, should take over the duties of the House Surgeon at the Hospital. As the students would not be paid and the teachers would offer their services free, the saving would be £100, the Resident House Surgeon's salary. In April 1855, Dr. Thomas Benson, the House Surgeon, left and the arrangement with the senior students went into effect. Resident Medical Officers from then on were recommended by the Faculty of Medicine at Queen's, usually the clinical lecturers, and appointed by the Board of Governors of the Hospital. Close attention by the doctors to the clinical work of their students improved the daily medical care to the advantage of the patients, the Hospital and the Faculty of Medicine.

An Act to amend the laws relative to the incorporation of the Trustees of the Kingston General Hospital was given final assent on 1 July 1856. The amended Act set out that one of the medical professors at Queen's College, to be nominated annually by the Senate thereof, would be a Governor; and further provided for the appointment by the Governor of the Province of eleven Life Governors, to be recommended by the Board. Also, any person who paid £25 and continued to pay an annual fee of £1 could be a Governor of the Kingston Hospital. The Governors were to elect their own Chairman and have the power to appoint such officers for the proper management of the Hospital as they deemed necessary. In most other provisions the amended Act followed closely the original Act of Incorporation.

The new Board of Governors met on 5 November 1856 and elected as their Chairman Dr. James Sampson, President of the Queen's Medical Faculty, thus forging a closer bond between the College and the Hospital. The new Life Governors were: Dr. Sampson, Hon. John Macaulay, Hon. J. A. Macdonald, John R. Forsythe, Thomas Kirkpatrick, John Watkins, James Hopkirk, Thomas Askew, John Paton, William G. Hinds, and James Harty. The appointment of eleven men of such calibre, some of whom devoted every spare moment to the work of the Hospital, marked a turning point in its affairs. Not that the financial problems were immediately solved, but no waste was overlooked, no problem ignored, no chance for improvement missed by the devoted attention and diligence of the men who volunteered to manage the Hospital. James Hopkirk, elected Secretary, was an almost daily visitor during his whole term of office.

The Board's first request was for a financial statement from the old Board of Governors. They also asked for any suggestions the old Board might have for the best way to pay off the debt and still maintain the efficiency of the Hospital until the 1857 government grant was paid to the Hospital. The report which Dr. Yates presented at the December meeting was discussed and filed in January. He reviewed the problems and the progress since he had come on the Board in 1854 and reported an increase in the number of patients cared for, an addition to the real and personal property of the Hospital, and a reduction of the debt from £736 to £551. He estimated that under strict economy and 'by a reduction in the number of patients so soon as the warm weather of the spring shall permit,' the Hospital might hope to be free of debt in three years.

The old Board recommended that applications for relief grants be made to the City and the County Councils, to private charity and to Parliament for an increase in the annual grant. This would be for the future. Meanwhile, they suggested, the new Governors must be prepared to pledge their individual credit and to advance money from their personal resources as their predecessors had done. Their charity would have to support the Hospital until they found other funds.

The statement of receipts and expenses, showing receipts in 1856 from patients to have been £124.12.7, is the first definite indication that a fair number of paying patients were being accepted at this charity Hospital. Some of them were undoubtedly maternity patients as a minute of the Board indicates: 'That it had been the practice to set the Tenner Ward apart for respectable female patients and that no woman of the Town should be admitted to it, but that such women should be confined to the Weber Ward – this rule to be enforced.' It also indicates the class of female patients – 'women of the Town' – who were a constant charge upon the Hospital. However, charity patients were not all from poor homes. A newspaper report that year mentioned that 'many respectable families are relieved of the expense and anxiety attendant on keeping sick servants in their houses, but how few are so grateful as to send even a small contribution in return.' These were some of the sick poor at the Hospital.

It seems likely that the paying patients came mostly from outside Kingston, seeking admission to the Hospital to secure the medical attention not available in the rural areas. An announcement of the Queen's Medical session confirms this and shows again the relationship between Queen's and the Hospital from the start of the Medical Faculty. 'The Kingston General Hospital, which receives the sick from parts intermediate between Toronto and Montreal, may be attended by the students of Queen's College, during their whole period of study, on payment of £1 at the commencement of the course. Four members of the Medical Faculty will be the medical attendants at the Hospital; and will thus have it in their power to afford regular Clinical instruction.'

However, the wording of that announcement regarding the payment of £1 was challenged by some members of the Medical Staff. The resulting controversy led to an open break in the Queen's Medical Faculty. Doctors Dickson and Yates, who gave the clinical courses, maintained that the students could not attend the Hospital to receive instruction unless they paid the six dollar fee for each clinical course. (In January 1858, currency was changed officially from pounds to dollars although the latter had already been in use for some years.) Dr. John Stewart, the peppery Secretary of the Faculty, called such fees extortion and removed Dickson's and Yates' names from the printed announcement of the courses. They protested this high-handed act. Dr. Stewart maintained that he was answerable only to the Trustees, and, indeed, since Dr. Sampson had asked to be removed from the Medical Faculty Council, there was no voice as strong as that of this irascible Scotsman who loved a fight. Dr. Dickson threatened to resign if Dr. Stewart were not reprimanded and the Board of Trustees ruled that the Board should henceforth approve any medical announcement before it was published. Dr. Stewart's refusal to account for funds he had spent further irritated his colleagues. Finally a series of charges of indiscreet behaviour, most of which he admitted, forced Dr. Stewart's resignation in 1861.

Dr. James Sampson, in 1857 nearly seventy years old, found his duties as Surgeon to the Penitentiary and as Chairman of the Board of Governors of the Kingston General Hospital enough to handle without being involved in the disorders of the Medical Faculty. In December 1857, he sent his resignation to the Queen's College Trustees but it was not finally accepted until November 1860.

With the very able assistance of Mr. Hopkirk, Secretary of the Board and a regular Visiting Governor, the management of the Hospital proceeded smoothly. A set of rules and regulations had been printed and distributed so that the staff knew the limits of their responsibilities. Distinctive clothes had been provided for the indigent patients so that the ambulatory ones would not be mistaken for the hired help. Tenders were called for supplies, quality and quantities checked, and the building was put in better repair: double windows were put on in the winter, the roof was repaired, and some painting done.

The Board of Governors met each month to receive the reports of the Visiting Governors who inspected the Hospital daily; to examine the Steward's petty cash book, the weekly diet tables; and to hear his report. They regularly considered the recommendations which resulted from this close scrutiny of its management. The Hospital had become a much bigger operation. The 1858 annual report stated: 'The Household consists of a house surgeon, a steward, a matron, four regular nurses, a cook, a washerwoman, orderlies, etc. One of the visiting surgeons attends at the Hospital every day and sees every patient. Each one takes the whole practice in turn for six weeks with the sole power of admitting or discharging.'

The minutes of the meetings of the Board of Governors and the annual reports, compiled generally by the House Surgeon, serve as a history of the management and organization of the Hospital. The only record which gives any detailed information on the patients in this period is a single book, the Admission Ledger. The complete Hospital record of a patient is there, in a single line across the page. The Admission Ledger for 1853 to 1866 records the diseases, the days in Hospital, the statistics of age, country of origin, religion, and a space for 'Remarks', – brief social history in itself. The Ledger is embellished by the doodling of a young House Surgeon, noting among other things, on an end paper, that a patient (no name) was admitted with 'leesons (sic) of the waterworks'. This is not so amusing when the number of primary, secondary, and tertiary cases of syphilis and gonorrhea are counted. There are other interesting items in the disease column. The first recorded mention in this Ledger of 'influenza' appears in an 1861 entry.

The editor of a local paper, commenting on the annual report of the Hospital which contained a list of the diseases treated, said that seventy-five per cent of the cases in the Hospital sprang more or less directly from vice. Of the three hundred and twenty-four adults admitted, over forty-five per cent were drunkards suffering from diseases and injuries, delirium tremens, frostbite, and burns attributable to their drunken state. Of twenty-nine babies born in the Hospital in one year nearly all were illegitimate – and as the editor pointed out, 'nearly all from the country'. Were they the offspring of the so-called women of the Town?

Infants were admitted with their sick mothers and sometimes whole families of young children were brought in simply 'for shelter'. Over thirteen per cent of the patients were children under ten years of age, suffering from bronchitis or pneumonia, fever, diarrhoea, diseases of the eye, frostbite and burns. A further seventeen per cent of the patients were under twenty; but the biggest group, almost thirty per cent, were between twenty and thirty years old. There were more male than female patients, especially in the older age groups; a not unusual diagnosis was simply 'debility'.

It was these older patients who stayed longer than the others and caused a continuing problem in Hospital administration. The widows and orphans could find a refuge in the House of Industry or in the Orphanage but, although the House of Industry would take a few, most of the old men had no place to go. A very few were kept on until warmer weather as part-time handymen, their board paid by the personal charity of doctors or governors. One amusing entry in the Remarks column says, 'Came into a fortune and left,' a happy ending for one patient.

Other Remarks are also social commentaries: 'In black book. Stole a pair of drawers from a patient.' 'Discharged for refusing to assist nurse.' It was accepted practice for the ambulatory patients to be given certain duties – cleaning, serving food, gardening. They were also often asked to watch over critically ill patients and instructed to call the nurse when necessary.

It is not clear what, if any, change there was in the medical treatment offered, beyond the daily attention of the visiting surgeon and the attendance of the students and their teachers. The Hospital provided clean accommodation, simple food and uniform clothing, with so-called nursing care for the very ill. The doctors used their own instruments, generally right at the bed, for any simple operation, though a section of one ward was set aside as a surgery. And, for a time, the doctors provided the prescribed medicines until tenders were called for the few standard drugs in common use.

It was accepted that contagious diseases had no place in a general hospital and those suffering from smallpox, for instance, were refused admission to the wards. When there was a case of smallpox in the Hospital, diagnosed after admission, all further patients admitted were vaccinated. The known contagious cases were generally sent elsewhere and there was an attempt to segregate the smallpox cases in the old fever shed beside the Hospital. The doctors and most of the Governors were very much aware of the urgent need for a proper isolation ward; and this awareness led to the plans for the new Watkins Wing.

There is no doubt that the association with Queen's Medical Faculty had a salutory effect on the progress of medical treatment at the Kingston General Hospital. Medical education, like all other education, tended to lag behind, with a certain resistance to new discoveries. Yet the staff, to maintain and increase the reputation of Queen's Medical Faculty, had to keep abreast of the developments in medicine and to make use, if possible, of the new instruments as they became available.

In 1856 the Medical Faculty had announced, 'The Professor of Anatomy will be assisted in the Dissecting Room by Dr. Meadows, one of the assistant surgeons of the 9th Regt. Dr. Meadows will give particular attention to the Microscope; the Faculty being supplied with two of the best instruments of British manufacture, in addition to others of inferior value.' The microscope had been invented less than twenty years before; one of the most important precision instruments to augment and make more exact the doctors' powers of observation. It was used first in morbid anatomy, but soon it opened a new world of medical research to form the basis for preventive medicine. The Queen's announcement shows also that Kingston was still benefiting from the presence of surgeons of the military garrison.

In January 1859, Dr. Sampson, Chairman of the Board, reported that the Hospital debt had been paid and that there was a balance of $1,000. That was good news but there was also an unpleasant situation facing the Board. The year began with an acrimonious controversy between the Hospital and the House of Industry, complicated by an unfortunate personal conflict between the surgeon at the House of Industry and one of the visiting surgeons at the Hospital. The basis of the dispute was financial. The Board of Governors of the Hospital had resolved that, since the House of Industry received a government grant for the benefit of the indigent sick in its care, the Directors of that House should pay board for their inmates admitted to the Hospital. The cutting part of the resolution was the direction that the patients from the House of Industry should be sent to the hospital 'in a cleanly state and with one change of underclothing'. The House of Industry replied with a charge that their inmates who went to the Hospital were often discharged from there in an unclean state and not cured. The controversy dragged on through the year with breaks in communication and postponements of joint meetings. The Mayor, Dr. O. S. Strange, was finally called on to settle the dispute.

James Hopkirk, Secretary to the Board and a devoted Visiting Governor, became ill and died in October 1859. It was a grievous loss for the Hospital Board and for the management of the institution. Dr. Sampson, lame from a bad fall and in declining health and strength, had become increasingly dependent on Hopkirk's supervision of the daily operation of the Hospital. According to entries in the book kept to record the remarks and suggestions of the visiting governors, Thomas Askew, one of the Life Governors, seems to have taken over Mr. Hopkirk's duties as a regular Visiting Governor, being in almost daily attendance at the Hospital.

The Minute Book for the Board of Governors' meetings from January 1860 to January 1863 is missing, if one ever existed. The minutes of some meetings are recorded in the Visiting Governors' Book and this may indicate that there were few formal meetings. Most of the information available for that period is contained in the annual reports compiled by the House Surgeon and printed in the local newspaper. Evidently the regular management of the Hospital was being competently handled by the chief Visiting Governor, Thomas Askew, and by the experienced Steward, Rody Hatton. The Steward's job was to take care of 'the provisioning and material wants of the inmates' and to be 'in charge of the bed linen and furniture'. The medical duties were handled by the young House Surgeon, an undergraduate who was supervised by the Visiting Surgeons. The House Surgeon was expected to 'attend to the warming and ventilation of the Hospital, so important to the well being of the patients. To prepare and administer medicines. To watch cases in the absence of the regular physicians. To admit patients, assign them to a ward, register them and fill out a ticket at each patient's bed – to be placed at the head of the bed'.

The House Surgeon from June 1860 to May 1861, was Alfred Sales Oliver of Kingston. As a boy, Oliver had ridden with Dr. Sampson on his rounds and was determined to follow in his footsteps. Oliver completed his medical studies at Queen's and was given special permission to write his final examinations in April 1861, when he was only nineteen years old. Although he passed, he could not be given his degree until he reached the age of twenty-one, as required by the Queen's College regulations. After completing his term as House Surgeon, Oliver went to England for further study in surgery. In the summer of 1862, having passed an examination in medicine in Albany, New York, he received a commission in the New York 20th Regiment and served with that unit at the Battle of Fredericksburg in December. In 1863, Oliver returned to Kingston to receive his degree and to open his practice.

Mr. Channonhouse followed Alfred Oliver as House Surgeon in May 1861, having been the most advanced undergraduate recommended to the Board of Governors by the Medical Faculty. The medical care of the patients was in good hands, the administration was running smoothly again and the government grant of $6,000, plus private donations, met the current financial needs of the Hospital. But the Board was faced with the greater problem of a need for more space.

Increasing numbers of patients were being admitted each year with the prospect of an even greater number in the near future. As a newspaper reported, 'The reluctance which was formerly evinced by the destitute to enter the hospital is now reversed, and numbers of a better class seek admission and pay to the institution a liberal sum for the advantages derived thereat. The Hospital is now exceeded by none in the Province in any desirable point.' The Board began to discuss the possible site, size, and arrangement of new accommodation. Architect William Coverdale was asked to prepare plans for the building and the search for funds was organized.

On 9 November 1861, Dr. James Sampson died, the acknowledged head of his profession in Kingston, recipient of an honorary M.D. from McGill University, Surgeon to the Provincial Penitentiary, former President of the Medical Faculty of Queen's College, Chairman of the Board of Governors of the Kingston General Hospital. The quiet and simple funeral he had requested could not be so limited, as Kingstonians turned out to honour the man who had served as magistrate, mayor, commissioner, member of the provincial Medical Board, surgeon and physician to rich and poor alike.

The care of the sick had to go on and the Hospital Board elected lawyer Thomas Kirkpatrick Chairman and reappointed Neil McLeod as Secretary. The Governors then considered the plans for the new wing to the Hospital. These plans had been prepared as a gift from the architect, William Coverdale, and called for a three storey building to 'contain a lecture room and amputating theatre. Besides its college appliances the new building will be apportioned off into fever and smallpox wards.' In April 1862, the Board announced that John Watkins, one of the Life Governors, would give $4,000, the estimated cost of the complete wing, and such other amount as was necessary to finish it. John Watkins (1789–1876), a hardware merchant, was noted for his generous gifts to St. George's Church, to Queen's College and to the Hospital. He was also a modest man and the plaque on the new wing acknowledging his gift had to be placed there without his knowledge.

Construction started on the building at once, with a promised completion date of the following November. The *Kingston Daily News* of 11 June 1862, described the building:

> The new wing measures 53 ft. in length by 50 ft. in breadth and consists of three storeys. The ground floor or basement will be apportioned into two small pox wards, respectively for male and female patients, with separate apartment for kitchen, storage etc. The next storey or first floor will be divided into four wards, intended for the admission of a respectable class of patient who may be able to pay a certain amount for the medical attendance and nursing, such as a young man who may be taken sick when boarding in hotels, away from their family and friends. The four wards, it is thought, will be

sufficient to keep separate the patients afflicted with different contaminating diseases. On the second or third storey will be fitted up an operating theatre for amputations and major operations in surgery. The plan of this room consists of an operating table, fixed in a good light in the extreme end, surrounded with converging benches for the accommodation of students of medicine. There are also small ante rooms for the convenience of the surgeons and professors. The theatre will be used as a clinical lecture room as well. The three storeys do not equal in height the adjoining Hospital building, the ridge of the roof of the wing reaches to the eaves of the main building, and is strictly, in an architectural sense a wing and not an elongation of the original building. The main entrance is at the front reaching the first floor by a vestibule and flight of stairs, and entering the basement by a separate door. The three outside walls will be all dressed stone with elegant windows and cornices.

The Hospital started the year 1863 with increased accommodation, built by a donation and furnished by other donations. The *Kingston Daily News*, taking pride in the operation of the Kingston Hospital, commenting on an article published in April in the *Toronto Globe*, said that they should compare the Toronto General Hospital to the Kingston General Hospital. In Kingston the House Surgeon and Secretary both served gratuitously, while in Toronto they had to be paid $1,000 each. The editor also commented on the up-to-date facilities in the services at the Kingston Hospital. 'The washroom is fitted with all the requisites of a laundry, having its boilers and wash tubs as well as a patent wringing machine ... This machine is at once most curious, useful and simple, while it requires little skill to operate it. It consists of a frame in which revolve two gutta-percha rollers ... turned by a handle ... Truly it is an appliance no laundry should be without.'

The year started well but trouble came soon: the government grant for 1863 was reduced by $1,200 to only $4,800. With the increased accommodation in the Watkins Wing, the operating expenses had risen and the doctors and governors made additional gifts to keep the Hospital out of debt. By October the Board had decided that the only solution was to take fewer free patients. But they offered to take additional indigent patients at only fifteen cents a day, adding that the charity-minded should be willing to make more donations for this service. One of the attending medical officers was at one time supporting ten of these additional patients. Donation boxes for the Hospital were placed in banks and other business houses and the press appealed to the citizens to come to the aid of this important charity. The counties were criticized for sending no subscriptions or gifts since almost fifty-three per cent of the indigent patients came from outside Kingston.

Notations in the Visiting Governors' Book over the next few years tell of the careful measures taken to keep the running expenses to a minimum while caring for as many indigent sick as possible. The Governors postponed the employment of another nurse and urged the female patients to work, so far as they were able, in their own wards. The Steward was authorized to hire a woman only one day a week to scrub floors and a yard man just two days to clean up the grounds and the garden. The Matron was instructed to hire two girls for a few days to do some mending. Gifts of cast-off clothing, barrels of apples, bushels of potatoes, thirty gallons of beer, and three hindquarters of beef were duly noted. But sometimes gifts did not supply badly needed items and a purchase was necessary. Fifty blankets bought at a surplus sale at the Naval Dockyard were a special bargain.

In April 1865, after the death of Rody Hatton, a new Steward, Louis Buttner, was installed. He was to serve the Kingston General Hospital for over twenty-five years as a sort of general manager. The Visiting Governors, anxious to make the best use of the Hospital accommodation and funds, kept careful check on those patients who were indigent and on those who could pay something, no matter how little. They were particularly watchful about patients who, they felt, should be transferred to other institutions. The medical men were equally watchful. An attending doctor noted that an insane person should have been moved out some-time before so as not to occupy one of the free beds.

It was not only the poor who wanted free beds. John Fraser, a Visiting Governor, in August 1866, reported three young men in one room in the Watkins Wing who 'say they are medical students and not expected to pay. Such patients cause a great deal of trouble and expense to the Institution and they themselves say there is very little if anything the matter with them. Besides themselves, they have a host of friends occasionally at meals with them.' The action taken on this matter is not recorded in the Minute Book but it seems likely that those patients were quickly discharged.

Queen's Medical Faculty had that year been completely disrupted by internal feuding and by major disagreements with the College Trustees regarding rules and regulations. Most of the staff had resigned and had set up their own medical school, the Royal College of Physicians and Surgeons of Kingston, incorporated by Act of Parliament in July 1866. It was affiliated with Queen's College for the granting of degrees but was otherwise a separate entity, renting from Queen's its premises, the new Medical Building, built in 1858. The arrangement with the Kingston General Hospital regarding student attendance was the same as before; but the Board of Governors appointed its own clinical lecturers. Dr. Horatio Yates succeeded Thomas Kirkpatrick as Chairman of the Board of Governors, strengthening the connection with the medical school.

In September 1866 the business community was stunned by the failure of the Bank of Upper Canada. The Hospital lost almost $1,000 and the disaster affected so many of those who gave regularly to the Hospital that the year ended on a very pessimistic note. The ten years, since the amended Act of Incorporation had been passed and the new Board of Governors installed, had seen good progress in the affairs of the Hospital. The administrative organization had functioned smoothly and the medical care offered had benefited from the improved management as well as from the association with the Queen's Medical Faculty. Accommodation had been increased by very generous donations. Yet the Kingston Hospital could not increase the number of free beds because the government grant was still only $4,800 and the city and counties made no grants in assistance. To depend on voluntary contributions to meet the steadily increasing costs was a poor prospect if the Kingston General Hospital hoped to grow with the country.

Four

As the year 1867 opened, one of the Life Governors of the Kingston General Hospital was very busy in England where he was chairman of the London Con- ference discussing the last details of the federal union of the Canadian Provinces. John A. Macdonald's attention was on the bill which, as the British North America Act, was presented to the British Parliament on February 12th and finally passed on March 8th, to be proclaimed on July 1st – Dominion Day. In Kingston few people were very excited about the Act, however much they might celebrate later; it had been accepted as a sure thing if John A. wanted it.

Kingston in 1867 had a population of about 12,000, counting the 3,000 men with their families in the garrison and those in the Penitentiary. Although the city limits had been extended to Palace Road seventeen years before, there were great open areas, with building outside the old city limited mostly to a few blocks on either side of the main roads. Along the waterfront, ship building and the busy locomotive works had replaced some of the old transshipment wharves. Most of the other industries were fairly small operations, such as carriage and waggon makers, manufacturers of stoves and tinware. There were also seventeen shoemakers, eleven dressmakers, and twenty-one milliners. Near the Hospital a knitting mill and a sewing machine factory occupied the waterfront. In the middle of the city were a piano and a cigar factory; the tannery and the broom factory were on the northern outskirts while in and around the city several breweries prospered.

There were some amenities for Kingstonians – a few 'improved' streets with board walks but muddy crossings. Livestock was no longer allowed to run at large. The city had gas lights for inside illumination and for some streets, and a water works system, with the pumping station at the foot of West Street. There was an elementary drainage system in the older part of the city, but only the well-to-do had water closets and the outdoor privies continued to be a menace to public health in spite of generous supplies of slaked lime. Yet Kingstonians were more aware of public health problems than many Canadians, better informed and more experienced. Served by four or five local newspapers they could read about the health measures not only in the rest of Canada but also in Britain and the United States. They had come through in the year just past, 1866, the threat of a cholera epidemic, which had been confined by strict isolation and health measures to only fifteen cases. The Kingston Board of Health, set up by a civic by-law in 1838, was a pioneer in public health work. Although it was only intermittently effective or even active, it justified its existence in such a crisis. Its work was, of course, confined to the city, unlike the Hospital which served a much larger area, mainly rural.

Other health and charity agencies in Kingston had been slowly expanding. The Hotel Dieu, on Brock Street, needed more space even though they could send their elderly indigents to the Sisters of Charity at the House of Providence. The House of Industry had been enlarged; and, in 1864, the Orphanage had moved into its new building at the corner of Union Street and the present University Avenue. It operated under the care of the Widows' and Orphans' Friends Society (formerly the Female Benevolent Society); Government health agencies were expanding too. At the Criminal Lunatic Asylum at Rockwood, beyond Portsmouth Village, which had been opened in 1856, a new wing for female inmates had just been added to the 1860 stone building.

The 1867 Medical Register of Upper Canada listed twenty-one doctors in Kingston and immediate vicinity, including Waterloo (the present Cataraqui Village), Wolfe Island, and Odessa. Seventeen of them were in Kingston but some of the well-known names had disappeared from the list – Dr. George Baker, Dr. Thomas W. Robison, Dr. James Sampson. Dr. J. R. Dickson had succeeded Dr. Sampson as Surgeon to the Penitentiary and was carrying on Dr. Sampson's enlightened treatment there. He was also Dr. Sampson's successor on the provincial Medical Board where he served as the first President of the Ontario Medical Council, successor to the Upper Canada Medical Board. The Province continued to have control of medical standards under a new act of 1866 which gave the Council of the College of Physicians and Surgeons of Ontario the authority to license medical practitioners in the province and to set the regulations regarding medical education.

At Queen's the Medical Faculty had suffered from the internal troubles at the College. In their new status as a separate medical school they were attempting to recover but were to receive a further blow when Queen's had a financial crisis. As the Royal College of Physicians and Surgeons of Kingston they rented the Medical Building from Queen's and used the equipment provided there, limited though it was. Troubles within the Queen's staff, complicated by bank failures and the cut in government funds to sectarian colleges, precipitated another crisis. When the government grant of $750 to the medical college was withdrawn in December 1869, the Royal College (Kingston) applied to Queen's for a remission of rent. Principal William Snodgrass and most of the Trustees saw no reason why they should support with their dwindling funds this dissident and mostly non-Presbyterian group of doctors who had already separated from Queen's. Not only was the Royal College refused free accommodation but they were also given notice to move out of the Medical Building. Queen's, then in great financial difficulties, decided that to stay open the College had to move classes to the Medical Building so that senior professors could be housed in Summerhill, rent free in lieu of salary.

The Royal College of Physicians and Surgeons of Kingston found temporary accommodation in an old building about two miles from the Kingston General Hospital. They moved the next year into the old Commercial Bank Building near the foot of Princess Street where they at least had gaslight and running water. Yet it was not a happy move and attendance fell in the next few years. Their dependence on the Hospital facilities increased so that the medical education they offered would not suffer.

Since the medical school had opened, just over twelve years before Confederation, medical education had progressed, though at a snail's pace by modern standards. Medical research was making it possible to describe the functions and diseases of various parts of the body. British and American medical publications were carefully studied by professors and students alike. Queen's medical professors had always stressed the importance of clinical studies in both medicine and surgery, and, in the Royal College, some of the doctors gave no lectures except at the clinical demonstrations at the Hospital. As particular importance was given to the study of anatomy, the dissecting room was open evenings so that the medical students could have sufficient time – even if they sometimes had limited material – for their study of anatomy. They probably could have explained the entry in the Hospital Death Book, regarding disposal of bodies, which said, 'Body disappeared.'

New modes of seeing diseases led to new methods of treatment and the discovery of anaesthetics led to new surgical techniques. The use of ether and chloroform meant that speed was no longer the prime necessity in operations; but the inability to control infections meant that much conservative surgery was not yet possible. The fact that most operating rooms were called amputating theatres until the 1890s, indicates the major surgical procedures. In 1867, Lister, in Edinburgh, introduced antiseptic surgery with his famous carbolic spray; but there was vehement debate and disagreement about its worth and it was seldom used elsewhere until many years later.

Surgical instruments had been refined and improved so that more delicate ones made the removal of cataracts a not too unusual operation at the Kingston General Hospital in the 1860s. Hypodermics had already come into use; the first clinical thermometer, ten inches long, was used in England in 1867. The next year it was reduced to pocket size and was soon in general use.

In spite of the progress in medicine, life expectancy at birth was only about forty years. Ague, or malaria, was prevalent, especially along the Rideau River, and regular doses of quinine were administered, somewhat indiscriminately, to ward off the intermittent fever. Druggists advertised fresh stocks of fine healthy Swedish Leeches; and the newspapers carried columns of advertisements for marvellous cure-alls. But the standard remedy for many ills, especially in rural homes, was a bottle of whiskey, a painkiller as useful for earache as for childbirth. The work of Pasteur and Koch would lead in the next twenty-five years to the discovery of the causes of some infectious diseases – relapsing fever, gonorrhea, typhoid, and erysipelas – but the prevention of those diseases was far in the future. Even the work of Dr. J. P. Semmelweis of Vienna, on the control of childbed fever, announced in 1847, was still generally ignored or misrepresented. The danger of contagion was recognized; there were isolation wards. But nurses and doctors moved between wards, without changing garments or, usually, even washing their hands.

As 1867 began the Kingston General Hospital, with the added facilities of the Watkins Wing, could accommodate about seventy patients, and the staff regularly treated a large number of outdoor patients. Yet they had to limit the free beds to fifty because funds were so low. They hoped that the seven private rooms for paying patients would bring in sufficient income to help meet expenses. The Board of Governors assumed what was to be their main job – to supervise the finances and to put pressure on government for assistance. They were men of influence, these Governors, men of business acumen, wealth, and social standing whose charitable interests were directed to the welfare of the Kingston General Hospital. For some Governors, who had retired from active business, their volunteer duties were a full-time occupation. The Chairman, Dr. Yates, was a daily visitor in the course of his medical practice. The Vice Chairman and the Secretary-Treasurer carried on their part of the management of the institution from their town offices. While the devoted Visiting Governors, such as Fraser, Chown, and Duff, provided the Board's day-to-day link with the actual operation of the Hospital, the Governors' main concern was with the financial health of the institution. The year 1867 was critical, for in the changeover in federal and provincial governments one year of the regular government grant to the Hospital was lost.

The Hospital had started the year in financial straits and by June the funds were gone. The Governors appealed to the city and to the counties for assistance, but no immediate reply was forthcoming. The July 1st celebrations for the new Dominion of Canada were not echoed at the Hospital, as it was not known whether, under the new order, any grant would be made to the Kingston Hospital by the new provincial government. In August the *Daily News* announced that the Board of Governors, having considered closing the Hospital, instead appealed for funds to allow it to stay open. Belleville sent $200, but the Kingston City Council delayed action on a request for $400 because the House of Industry was also asking for help.

The Toronto General Hospital refused to accept any patients and closed down as they, too, had not received a government grant for 1867. And some very sick people, who ordinarily would have gone to Toronto, were admitted to the Kingston General Hospital. In Kingston only the really serious cases were admitted and others were treated at their homes. The result of this policy was that this year, for the first time, there were more surgical than medical cases in the Hospital. Stricter economy was instituted wherever possible, but economy could not make up for an almost total lack of income and the debt began to rise. If it had not been for the credit extended by the Commercial Bank, the Kingston General Hospital would have closed in the spring of 1867.

Then a further blow struck, affecting not only the Hospital but also Queen's College and many in the community; on 22 October 1867 the Commercial Bank suspended payment. The Hospital was destitute; Queen's lost its endowment fund; it had already lost its government grant when the provincial government decided not to support sectarian colleges. Should Queen's close? Should the Hospital close? Queen's Trustees met in a two-day emergency session and started an endowment drive to keep the College open. The Board of Governors of the Hospital met and pledged funds to meet the immediate expenses.

The citizens of Kingston petitioned Mayor John Breden, in December 1867, to call a public meeting to make sure that the Hospital would not close. It had remained open until then, supported by gifts from friends such as John Watkins, from organizations such as the Masons and from business firms like Calvin and Breck, who gave what was to become their annual Christmas Gift to the Hospital. The counties gave grants totalling $975. The public meeting agreed on the absolute necessity of keeping the Hospital open: it treated patients from the city and country who had nowhere else to go. It was of great importance to the medical school, serving as the source of clinical study for over eighty students. Dr. Yates, Chairman of the Board of Governors, told the meeting that the Hospital needed their immediate support for, in spite of economy measures, in spite of discharging the matron, one nurse, and the yardman, the funds and the credit were exhausted and the Hospital was $1,250 in debt.

Citizens rallied to the support of their charity Hospital and the men set up a committee to canvass all households and businesses for donations of goods or money. Appeals were sent to all levels of government. The farmers in the district organized provision parties to donate cordwood, potatoes, anything they could. Music and literary groups gave benefit concerts, and the Meagher Brothers gave a skating exhibition before they left on their next American tour.

Publicity later gave added emphasis to the importance of any gift, however small. Consequently, the donation of a few bed sheets, a quilt, twenty-five pounds of fish, ten pounds of dried berries, and a carcass of mutton were acknowledged with grateful thanks. There were benefit concerts in Kingston, Gananoque, and Napanee; and some 'very young ladies on Johnson Street' held a bazaar in aid of the Hospital. Aid came from the country too; thirteen farmers in Storrington Township sent loads of cordwood and one farmer sent a load of hay to refill the bed ticks. The Hospital relying on private charity had managed to stay open but what would the next year bring?

In February 1868, a government grant of $4,800 was announced for the Kingston General Hospital. Although the Governors had hoped that the grant would be larger, their worst anxieties were relieved. The Toronto General Hospital was open again and the Kingston House of Industry had its grant renewed. But the Hospital debt remained. Since the government grant had never been enough to cover expenses, public support continued to be needed and to be received; and economy was still necessary. The Visiting Governors' Minute Book contained authorization for the purchase of only the absolute necessities, in small amounts, at the best possible prices. In June the Steward was instructed to have a roothouse built to store a large amount of garden stuff, presumably from the Hospital garden as well as from anticipated gifts.

The Hospital buildings could not be neglected but only minimal maintenance could be done, and that as economically as possible. An agreement was made with one Snider for whitewashing at $35 'all the old building from top to basement and five rooms in the Watkins Wing, with all the outhouses'. John Fraser signed the agreement for the Hospital, satisfied that he had made a good deal.

Inspector General Langmuir, after his October 1868 visit, complimented the Kingston General Hospital on its economy, its medical care, and its cleanliness and excellent order. He noted that he had not seen their financial report. The report, sent to him later, showed that the debt had been wiped out and all expenses met from current revenue. But the Governors knew that the cost of meeting the debt could be measured in the sad deficiencies in the buildings and the furnishings. There was no lack of patients; the year ended with the wards so crowded that a Visiting Governor noted that the Attending Physicians should be reminded that no more beds were available.

Over the next few years, while the Royal College of Physicians and Surgeons of Kingston was having housing troubles and struggling to maintain standards and to keep students, the Hospital was slowly recovering from its crisis of 1867. The

House Surgeons' yearly reports published in the local newspaper, showed a small increase in the number of paying patients and no severe epidemics. The editor of the *Daily News*, commenting on a report that the Hospital had been remarkably free of epidemic disease, said this was a strong argument in favour of treatment that was mainly hygienic, and that scrupulous attention to cleanliness, temperature, ventilation, food and drink was better than medicine. The only real extravagance at the Kingston General Hospital, he said, was in the amount of water used, but he approved of that.

When the Imperial troops were withdrawn from Canada in 1870, Kingston was without a British garrison for the first time in almost a hundred years. The young ladies of Kingston lost their best matrimonial chances (until the Royal Military College opened in 1876), the suppliers lost army contracts, and the brewers lost their best customers. Kingston medical men regretted the departure of their military colleagues who had given great assistance over the years. However, there were enough civilian doctors in Kingston to provide adequate health care and they were keeping abreast of medical developments and going abroad for advanced study.

The stimulating interplay of teaching and practice, with the Royal College medical professors also the attending physicians at the Hospital, served to give the citizens of the Kingston area superior medical care. Hospital visitors reported that the doctors were treating some of the victims of severe burns by skin grafting; and the success achieved indicates not only skill but also successful measures against infection. The Kingston General Hospital had the lowest death rate of Ontario Hospitals, and the city of Kingston the lowest death rate of any reported.

The editor of the *Daily News* was proud of that record but he was extremely critical of another record caused by the action, or inaction, of City Council regarding a grant to the Kingston Hospital. In eighteen years the City had given only $100, not every year but only once. Kingston was, in 1871, the only city in Canada with a hospital which it did not support with a yearly grant, however small. The editor continued, 'The Board of Health is a body without power or influence, appointed for the purpose of sharing responsibility and giving unheeded advice.' Obviously the City could not be counted on for financial support of any health service.

Consequently, the Governors had to look elsewhere for funds to ease their financial problems. They were reminded that the Kingston Hospital Act of Incorporation mentioned specifically 'the mariners of the Lakes' and that the federal government had jurisdiction over the establishment and maintenance of marine hospitals. They made an immediate application for a grant on that basis and received $500 from the federal government in 1873 and every year for some fifteen years thereafter. By a regular appeal to the counties the Hospital could generally expect to receive with each appeal about $500; but the grants were never certain.

There was increasing pressure from Government, from health authorities and from the general public for the absolute isolation of smallpox cases, not just in separate wards in the Hospital but in a completely separate building. The provision of such an isolation facility was, by law, the responsibility of the federal government, which it, in turn, had passed on to the cities and counties. So negotiations began with the City and with the counties because the Governors were not prepared to spend the Hospital funds to fulfill the quarantine responsibilities of these local governments. The Kingston City Council agreed in 1872 to make a yearly grant of $100, in lieu of rent, toward the operation of a smallpox hospital. While talks continued with the counties the Governors considered providing convenient accommodation for such a hospital.

The Garratt property, on King Street just west of the Hospital, was available and seemed to the Governors, on the advice of the doctors, to be a suitable place, conveniently close yet isolated. The citizens, especially those who lived in the southwest section of the city, did not agree. They raised an immediate outcry against locating a smallpox hospital, which, they said, would infect the atmosphere, near their favourite summer walk. Fort Henry, empty of British troops, was suggested as an alternative but to no avail. The doctors assured the citizens that there would be no danger of infection from walking near the smallpox hospital; and so the building was made ready for the first patients.

The maintenance of the old Hospital building was causing the Governors some concern, especially the method of heating it. The many stoves were uneconomical, unsatisfactory, and dangerous. On 28 February 1873 fire broke out in the Tenner Ward when a firepan under a stove burned through, set fire to the floor and the fire ran under the floor and into the walls. Alderman James Richardson, who lived next to the Hospital, responded to the calls for help. He and his sons, George and Henry, carried water to help contain the fire until the fire company arrived. The repairs cost $554 and forced the Governors to make some decisions regarding basic services in the Hospital.

There was no question about the urgent necessity of supplying running water to the upper floors of the Hospital. With stoves in every ward, lengths of stove pipe, candles, and coal oil lamps, the danger of fire demanded more adequate protection than any number of full fire buckets could provide. While the Governors were considering the best and most economical method of getting more water to the upper floors and of lighting the Hospital there was a chimney fire. They decided to recommend the immediate purchase of a small chemical fire engine because regular maintenance caused enough problems without the complications of even minor fire damage. Painting was needed and the old water closets were giving trouble.

The year 1873 was notable in the history of the Kingston General Hospital for more reasons than the Tenner Ward fire and the new smallpox hospital. It marked the beginning of a close association with the Hospital for two doctors who were to have a strong influence on its affairs for the next twenty-five years. One was Kenneth Neander Fenwick of Kingston, who was appointed House Surgeon for the Hospital for the months of April to October 1873, following the completion of his studies at the Royal College of Physicians and Surgeons of Kingston. During his time as House Surgeon he wrote up some case reports for a new Kingston publication, the *Canadian Medical Times*, an eight-page weekly published by Dr. James Neish, a recent graduate. Besides the local case reports, it contained reprints of British articles, such as one by Esmarch relating to his work with the elastic bandage for controlling bleeding from the extremities during surgery; and an interesting editorial on the training of nurses. The *Canadian Medical Times* ceased publication in November. Although Fenwick's tour of duty as House Surgeon was a temporary association, he went from that service to study in England and Scotland and returned to Kingston to give devoted and distinguished service to the Kingston General Hospital.

The other doctor was Alfred Sales Oliver, who had been House Surgeon from June 1860 to May 1861. He had completed his medical course that year but did not receive his degree until 1863 when he was twenty-one. Dr. Oliver had been recommended by some of his colleagues in 1864 for the Chair of Surgery on the Queen's Medical Faculty, after the resignation of Dr. J. R. Dickson, but he was considered to be too young – only twenty-two. Dr. Donald Maclean was appointed instead. In June 1873, Dr. Oliver was appointed an Attending Medical Officer at the Kingston General Hospital in the place of Dr. C. H. Lavell, who had resigned. Dr. Oliver's interest in surgery led him to campaign for better facilities for this work at the Hospital. But it was not easy. He found that there were many other inadequacies, not the least of which was money. Medical, management, and financial problems interacted and the old and continuing problem of an adequate government grant threatened the very existence of the Hospital.

Economic pressures in the 1870s forced the province to reorganize the patchwork of grants then in force. The provincial Charity Aid Act of 1874 provided that 'every institution named in Schedule "A" (which included the Kingston Hospital) shall so have and receive twenty cents for each day's actual treatment and stay of every patient, etc. etc.' An additional ten cents a day per patient was also to be granted, providing that such an additional grant did not make total provincial contributions exceed one-quarter of total revenues received from all sources other than the province. With such a provision the Kingston Hospital certainly did not qualify for the additional ten cents a day. The Hospital income from all other sources was extremely limited and never sure; it did not even equal the old government grant of $4,800. In the Hospital's past financial year, which ran from 1 October to 30 September, the total income, with the provincial grant, had been $8,551.52, of which $400 was specifically for the separate smallpox hospital.

When a letter from the Provincial Secretary informed the Governors that the possible withdrawal of the $4,800 grant for 1875 was being considered, the Governors threatened to resign in a body. There were some very urgent negotiations and even when the government grant was continued some reserve funds had to be found.

With the 'patient-day' payment in effect under the 1874 Act, the Inspector General of Hospitals began to be more critical in his assessment of the fitness of some patients to be a continuing charge on the Hospital. In 1875 he reported that of the forty-nine patients then in the Kingston General Hospital all but five were proper subjects for the Hospital. The careful inspection was viewed with alarm in the case of one patient. Mr. Glenn, with the approval of the Steward, requested the Board of Governors to let him 'be a servant not a patient so I can keep out of the way of the Inspector when he comes round. I can do lots of little things to earn the bit that I eat.' Willie Glenn became a servant and served the Hospital for over forty years.

In March 1877, the Inspector reported that 'sixteen patients have been residents of the Hospital since the first of October last – at least nine of whom are not proper subjects for a curative establishment. Pregnancy cases are admitted much in advance of the time required for treatment.' Two years later the provincial government put a limitation of 270 days on the time it would pay for any one patient. There was no easy solution about what to do with these 'unfit' patients and it was to be a continuing problem. A few years later Dr. Fife Fowler complained that the Hospital seemed to be a supplementary poor-house, especially in the winter. Patients, he thought, should be discharged sooner. Actually the patients at the Kingston General Hospital stayed a shorter time than those in the other hospitals in Ontario.

The Hospital's funds in 1877, were increased by a bequest of $4,000 from the estate of John Watkins, the Hospital's long-time benefactor who had died in June 1876. The Governors decided that the bequest should form the basis for an endowment fund to be invested at the best possible interest. Their financial statement for that year was the first one to include interest in the income column and from then on some very astute investments in mortgages brought good returns. The 1877 statement also included $817.25 from paying patients, $401.46 from the sale of a lot, and an item labelled 'profits from the garden and livestock'.

The year 1877 was important for a sister institution when the Rev. George Monro Grant became Principal of Queen's University. (Although Queen's had full university status from the beginning, it was referred to as Queen's College until

1874, when its constitution was revised.) Within two years Queen's had a new building, the present Theology Hall, and Principal Grant was persuading the Royal College of Physicians and Surgeons of Kingston to return to quarters in the Medical Building, in spite of the opposition of Dr. Michael Sullivan, President of the Royal College. With the return of the medical school to the campus of the University in 1880, the number of medical students, which had dropped to 33 in the 1874–1875 session, began to increase slowly.

Queen's general student enrolment had been increased in 1870 by the admission of women to some special lectures and by the 1878–1879 session, all Arts courses were open to them. In 1880, the Royal College of Physicians and Surgeons of Kingston announced that it would give, starting that April, a summer course of studies for women medical students. Four students registered to be taught by Prof. N. F. Dupuis and Doctors Fowler, Oliver, and T. R. Dupuis. The next April only two women registered for the summer course so they were allowed to take their lectures with the men students, beginning in October. Most of the medical students, however, objected to the invasion of their sacred premises and vowed to repel the invaders. Opposition to this co-education was sufficiently organized in the 1882–1883 session to force the women out by offensive demonstrations and actions on the part of a group of the men students and two staff members. When the men medical students threatened to move to Trinity College, the women were given separate lectures for the rest of the session and no more women were admitted to medicine.

The women would not admit defeat, however, and began a campaign to start their own school. In June 1883, a gathering of citizens resolved to open a separate medical school for women in Kingston. Nine women registered for classes held in City Hall and three received degrees the next spring: Mrs. Alice McGillivray, Miss Beatty, and Elizabeth Smith (later Mrs. Adam Shortt). There were never more than twenty-five students in any session and each year some were graduated, but the school was too small to carry on. The success of the Toronto Women's Medical College, which had also started in 1883, led to the closing of the Kingston Women's Medical College in 1895, five years after it had moved to Newcourt, beyond Portsmouth Village.

There was another medical organization in this period, even more temporary than the Women's Medical College. On 10 September 1880, the Kingston doctors met to organize the Cataraqui Medical Society. It was not the first such organization in the area; fifty years before the Midland District Medical Society had met a few times. Dr. J. R. Dickson was the first president of the Cataraqui Medical Society, Dr. Michael Lavell the vice-president. The secretary was Dr. W. H. Henderson and the committee members were Doctors O. S. Strange, Michael Sullivan, T. R. Dupuis, and Chamberlain Irwin. For the next six months they met regularly in each other's homes, read papers and discussed cases. Their minute book has no entries beyond May 1881. Their president, Dr. Dickson, who had retired from his post as Surgeon to the Penitentiary, became ill and died at the home of his son on Wolfe Island in November 1882. He had been the moving force in the Medical Society and without him the organization became dormant until it was revived some seven years later.

The records of the Kingston General Hospital indicate the beginning of a change in its role; it was no longer a simple refuge for the sick poor. More and more paying patients were seeking admission. Doctors were encouraging their patients to come to the Hospital for surgery which some years before they would have performed in the home. The Hospital was also beginning to provide some extra facilities. In 1880 the Board of Governors authorized the purchase of some surgical instruments – before that each doctor had used his own. Not that this initial purchase was large or was even well looked after but it marked a step forward in the provision of surgical facilities. An indication of things to come was made in June 1881, when Dr. Yates and Dr. Strange were authorized to set apart a portion of the Hospital for treatment of diseases of the eye and ear.

The number of paying patients increased but still more were needed to provide additional income. Consequently, there was a demand from doctors and patients for improved accommodation and better service. Food cooked in the basement kitchen, not very good to start with, was less palatable by the time it had been carried on trays up two or three flights of stairs. The regular diet for the charity patients seems to have been porridge, beef stew, dark bread, skim milk, and tea. The luxuries, such as fruit or fish, cost extra. In 1881 a hoist was installed to get meals and other supplies more speedily to the upper floors.

In 1884 gas lights were installed in the Hospital but when, in August that year, the Board received a gas bill for $19.92, the Governors decided that they must control such extravagance. They made a rule that 'In the future gas lights be used only after retirement for night of officials and servants of the institution and that at other times coal oil be used as formerly.' The main building continued to be heated by stoves until hot water coils were installed in 1885.

To achieve better service, the Hospital needed not only better facilities but also better help. There were no trained nurses; the 'nurses' employed at the Kingston General Hospital were generally middle-aged women who became toughened by the need to manage the drunks and women of the streets, for a long time the most numerous and frequent patients. One doctor recalled those nurses as 'old Sairy Gamps'. They had no training as nurses but some of them gave long and faithful service under difficult conditions. Take, for example, Mrs. Ewing. Her name first appeared in the Hospital records in 1864 and she seemed to be a regular employee then. The notation in the Visiting Governors' Book said, 'Another nurse is absolutely needed, the work being too hard for Mrs. Ewing.' In 1877, E. Chown wrote in the

Book, 'Buttner should get a nurse to assist Mrs. Ewing.' In June 1880, Mrs. Ewing asked that another nurse be engaged to relieve her of some duties in view of her increasing age; two years later the Steward was told to hire a nurse to help her. In 1883, the five women nurses, including Mrs. Ewing, were paid $9 a month each. In 1884 Mrs. Ewing's name appears for the last time when Ellen Pollard was hired to help her. The qualifications of the male nurses are indicated by the notation on a pay list that McRae, who did general work at $4 a month, was 'to be paid 50 cents extra for each coffin he made and $2 extra for nursing small pox patients when required'.

The general manager of the Kingston Hospital and the principal paid employee of the Board of Governors was the Steward. Louis Buttner, hired in 1865, served the Hospital faithfully and well. But, after some fifteen years service he assumed a proprietary attitude which became increasingly irritating to some of the doctors, especially to Dr. A. S. Oliver. The trouble with the volunteer, part-time management by the Board was its frequent change. Consequently, the permanent employee, the Steward, had become a virtual dictator. He knew and controlled more of the day-to-day management than the Visiting Governors. He hired and fired the nurses and other help; he did most of the purchasing; he had immediate charge of the building and of the help. He acted for the Board of Governors and could, in subtle ways, exert some authority even over the medical attendants. Those he disliked, especially among the younger men, he could frustrate in various ways. Entries in the Visiting Governors' Book indicate a slowly and steadily increasing dissatisfaction with the physical state of the Hospital. And there were some questions regarding the Steward's management.

Dr. Horatio Yates, who had been Chairman of the Board since 1866, was inclined to discount the complaints about Buttner. The two men, Doctor and Steward, had worked many years together. But on 11 March 1882, Dr. Yates died of pneumonia. Buttner no longer had a strong advocate on the Board to protect his position. It was, however, the medical attendants – the younger doctors and the House Surgeons – who finally brought the matter to a head.

In July 1882, Dr. A. S. Oliver preferred charges against Steward Buttner for officiousness and inefficiency. The affair was presumably settled outside the Board meeting for there is no further record of it. Dr. O. S. Strange, the new Chairman of the Board, and one of the senior physicians, exerted a calming influence. But trouble flared again in January 1883, when the House Surgeon and the Steward brought their disagreement to the Board to be settled. Buttner was having trouble with the servants, too, who finally complained formally to the Board that the Steward was not giving them tea for dinner as they had been promised. Constant small complaints brought a confrontation in July 1884. The Physicians of the Hospital met with the Board to ask for better management of the Hospital. They were asked to put their suggestions on paper and submit them for the Board's consideration. Buttner submitted, then withdrew, his resignation.

Suggestions which were made by the five Attending Physicians regarding the management of the Hospital and which were published in the local newspaper, are a good commentary on the operation of that institution in 1884. Dr. Fife Fowler, senior physician, suggested a few physical changes, concerning windows and cleanliness, but his main emphasis was on the number, crowding, and length of stay of patients. He thought also that there should be a woman in charge of the nurses who would supervise them and report to the doctors. 'The present Steward,' he said, 'is good and economical but unyielding and interfering.'

Dr. A. S. Oliver's list of suggestions was the longest and most detailed. He made little comment on the physical surroundings other than that the Hospital was gloomy, but he complained about the food. 'Diet is coarse, insufficient, unpalatable as served in tin dishes with the soup and meat together. The beef tea is sloppy with chunks of grease.' He also objected to skim milk. He felt that the general nursing care required great changes; there were not enough nurses and some were inefficient; they should not do a charwoman's job and they should wear distinctive dress. A lady superintendent or matron was needed and there should be a night watch 'for patients are indifferent and careless in watching' and 'patients shouldn't be allowed to take medicine themselves.'

Dr. Oliver reserved his most cutting criticism for the Steward, who, he said, caused too much delay at night in admitting accident cases; put constant obstructions in the way of students pursuing study at the Hospital, and clashed with the House Surgeons. He gave two examples: the Steward had opposed the House Surgeon's order of a physic; the Steward had refused to provide a stretcher as ordered for a very sick patient, saying a chair would do, and called the House Surgeon 'a puppy' for disagreeing with him.

Dr. T. R. Dupuis had no complaints about the Steward's general duties but he suggested that the surgical instruments (which had been entrusted to the Steward's care three years before) 'should be cared for by a permanent officer and would not then so often be lost or spoiled by rust'. Instruments under proper care, he said, might then accumulate by gift or purchase. He thought that the new operating room was not suitable and that the Attending Physicians should meet with the Board of Governors to consider not only an improved location for it but also other matters, such as the dispensary room and ventilation.

Dr. K. N. Fenwick, who had been an Attending Physician since the death of Dr. Yates, said that he had no trouble with the Steward who 'carried out instructions and was gentlemanly to the ladies'. However, he did object to the diet given the patients, to the old and drafty wards, and said, 'The operating room failed badly for the purpose at a late trial.'

Dr. H. G. Saunders started by saying that the Steward was good and economical but was disposed to clash with others. Then he went on to say, 'The Steward exceeded his authority in interfering with post mortems;' the meals were poor and the patients were afraid to complain to the Visiting Governors for fear of being 'spotted' by Mr. Buttner. The Doctor suggested that a permanent House Surgeon was needed because 'most of the casual ones quarrel with the Steward; in two cases they would not speak or eat together' and 'the Steward exceeds his duties because of the lack of experience of the House Surgeons'. Dr. Saunders also made suggestions about changes in nursing care, saying that one nurse should be kept up all night, taking duty in turn, to avoid the repetition of one recent case when a very ill woman had been left alone all night with no one to give her medicine or water. The nurse who was supposed to be on the ward was asleep and had complained of being overworked and tired out. He suggested that some ladies should act as visiting governors and make suggestions about the housekeeping and nursing.

The Board of Governors took immediate action on some of the suggestions. While keeping Mr. Buttner under close supervision, they started a search for both a new Steward and a Matron. They dismissed the most inefficient nurse and hired another. Though the Governors took no action that fall on the other suggestions, they continued discussions on how to make the changes and where to find the funds to accomplish the suggested improvements at the Hospital.

Five

In the next fifteen years the Kingston General Hospital was involved in its first big *Expansion* expansion in buildings, facilities, and services. Major reorganization of manage- *and* ment at all levels affected the Board of Governors, the doctors, nurses, and all the *Moderniza-* Hospital staff. *tion*

Some of the suggestions made in July 1884 by the Attending Physicians required *1885–1899* extended and careful study by the Board because their implementation would mean far reaching changes in the Kingston General Hospital. Others needed prompt but considered action. A new Steward must be carefully chosen and it was also obviously necessary to consider a revision and careful outline of his duties, responsi- bilities and authority. The decisions would affect the whole organization of the Hospital and also its relationship with the Queen's medical professors and their students.

How could the Hospital have more and better nurses, hire a Matron to supervise them, and improve the ward patients' diet without greatly increased expenditures? Where were the funds to improve the heating and ventilation, to brighten the wards, dress up the private rooms, and provide a proper operating room? If the ladies were asked to visit the Hospital what authority should they have? Since the Hospital was not yet on firm financial ground the Governors had to consider how the government and the general public, especially the benefactors, would support these suggested changes.

The provincial government, then in a power struggle with the federal govern- ment, was not likely to make an increased grant available. Kingston, fifth in size among cities of Ontario, had its own problems. The City Council was concerned, among other things, with controversy over a new union station about to be built for the Grand Trunk and the Kingston and Pembroke railways. Most of the people in the community were following with intense interest the troubles in the Northwest, especially when a group of volunteers from Kingston left to join the forces.

The Board of Governors, conservative as they were forced to be, approached the physicians' suggestions with extreme caution. The Board's first action in 1885 was to appoint as Steward and assistant, Mr. and Mrs. A. G. Watson. The Watsons, a comparatively young couple, had been trained in England and were currently employed in Jacksonville, Florida. Their combined pay was to be $480 a year, with board and room at the Hospital; and they were to take up their duties sometime in May. Meanwhile Steward Buttner stayed on until he was retired the first of June.

Dr. K. N. Fenwick thought that he had a solution to the nursing problem. On March he wrote to the Board suggesting that a training school for nurses be opened at the Hospital. The idea certainly had merit and needed consideration. The Board appointed Dr. O. S. Strange and Colonel John Duff to meet with Doctors Fife Fowler, T. R. Dupuis, and K. N. Fenwick to study the proposal and report at the next Board meeting.

Evidently the idea of setting up a school was considered by the committee to be too ambitious, for Dr. Fenwick's report, read at the meeting of May 7th, proposed establishing merely a class for training nurses. The proposal was accepted and referred back to the committee for more details. The *British Whig* reported the next day: 'Mr. and Mrs. Watson who soon enter upon duty at the General Hospital, being trained nurses, it has been resolved to open this summer in the building, a training class for nurses ... We have been advocating this step, as much in the interests of the public, as the Hospital, since nurses and especially intelligent ones, are scarce.' However, the proposal was not to be put into effect quite so soon, as the Board thought that some further consideration was necessary.

In August the *Daily News* reported that there had been a general meeting at the Hospital where a proposal to establish a training school for nurses had been discussed. The Medical Faculty had been requested to submit full particulars regarding cost, etc. for discussion at the next Board meeting but that report required further cautious study. Finally, in November 1885, the Board passed a resolution to place in the daily papers an advertisement for applications from two young women, to be between the ages of eighteen and thirty years, to be trained as nurses at the Kingston General Hospital. The applications were to be sent to the Steward, Mr. Watson, and the Board would then consider which two of the applicants to accept. (With the various delays, the first probationer was not accepted until well into 1886.)

Meantime another of the doctors' suggestions had been put into effect, unofficially. Some of the doctors' wives were visiting the Hospital frequently, having a look at the food and the way it was served. Mrs. A. S. Oliver, after one visit to the kitchen and an argument with the cook, decided that something should be done immediately to improve the situation. She called a meeting of interested women and organized a garden party to raise funds. The Folger Brothers' boats provided free transportation to Channel Grove, where Mr. Briggs provided free butter and milk. With other donations and many cash contributions the ladies cleared over $300. As a result the Hospital received the first china dishes for the ward patients, proper knives, forks and spoons, a big hall clock and six small ones to supplement the single clock then in the Hospital. And having given these things the ladies then suggested that an inventory of the Hospital supplies would be useful if they were to make other donations. The Board minutes noted, 'An inventory book to be secured.'

Whether the ladies, through their husbands, suggested it, or whether the public interest encouraged the Board, there were other improvements made that year. The Board authorized the installation of a telephone, on only six months' trial it is true, but the first telephone then in Kingston was only four years old. Hot water coils replaced the stoves in all the wards in the Main building and, in November, arrangements were made to place a night nurse on regular duty.

Early the next year, 1886, the visits of the ladies received the official approval of the Board. However, there was a careful distinction made to avoid possible bias on the part of the attending medical staff: no doctors' wives were included. Mrs. H. Skinner, Mrs. Macnee, Mrs. Graffety, Mrs. J. M. Machar, Miss Rice, Miss Robertson and Miss Muckleston were asked to visit the Hospital regularly and 'from time to time' to make suggestions to the Board. Mrs. Machar accepted the invitation for the ladies and visits began.

Dr. Fenwick was also making suggestions to the Board. For instance, he thought that they should offer more money to the nurses who would enter the Training School. The Board took no action on that suggestion for they were then considering an application for admission from Miss Watson and also a communication from Mrs. Watson, the Steward's wife. She wanted answers to specific questions about the rights and privileges of medical students in their attendance on paying patients as compared to charity patients. The questions asked and the answers given by the Board show that the medical students were taking advantage of the lack of rules to examine whom they pleased, when they pleased, in spite of objections by paying patients. This is the first definite indication that there were not quite enough of the free patients to satisfy the clinical teaching needs of the growing Medical School.

The progress of the Nurses' Training School is told in a letter dated 8 May 1886, from Dr. Fenwick to the editor of the *British Whig*, indicating some concern about the quality of applicants to the School:

About a year ago I proposed to the Governors the advisability of starting a school for training nurses in connection with the Kingston General Hospital.

Although they have been slow in moving, within the last two weeks they have decided to begin the scheme. An efficient head nurse who is a graduate of a Canadian training school, has been engaged and the first probationer has been received, while several applications have been received which are now under consideration. I think it only needs to be better known in order to have plenty of candidates for training and if the hospital material was utilized the work could be as efficiently carried on here as elsewhere.

The St. Catherines training school is the oldest in Canada and although a much older hospital than ours, their nurses have the reputation of being excellent. The plan here is to admit young women for a month on trial, and if found suitable are boarded and paid a salary, receiving instruction from the head nurse, house surgeon and visiting surgeons for a period of two years.

They are also, during a certain period, sent out to learn private nursing, and at the end of two years, after an examination, they secure a diploma which enables them to secure positions as trained nurses in public institutions or private families.

It must be a source of gratification to all concerned with the Hospital to see the citizens of Kingston take more interest in an institution which is doing such good work. Lately a committee of married ladies was appointed to visit regularly and make suggestions, while every Wednesday the young folks constituting the Flower Mission visit the institutions and gladden the hearts of the inmates.

Surely then, there are some who could go still further and spend a couple of years in acquiring a knowledge of nursing; even though they may not intend to follow it up for a livelihood.

Many opportunities will arise in their own homes, or among their friends, where such knowledge will be of inestimable value and of far more utility than many of the useless accomplishments which ladies are taught at the present time.

To those who wish to make it a vocation it opens a field of usefulness which is at once honorable, noble and remunerative, while at the same time the community reaps the benefit of having a class of person properly trained and fitted to carry out the physicians' instructions and to attend to the warmth, cleanliness and ventilation of the sick room, to prevent contagion and by careful and intelligent observation of symptoms to report these to the physician at his visit.

Perhaps it is only those who have had the services of a thoroughly trained nurse during a severe illness that can appreciate their value and how suffering can be mitigated and even life prolonged.

I will just say, in conclusion, that every effort will be made for the comfort of the probationers to ensure their thorough training in the art of nursing and to place the Kingston training school second to none in Canada.

Kenneth Neander Fenwick, MD

We might speculate on the effect of this recommendation by a prominent doctor. Certainly nursing had not been regarded as an occupation for the class of young women to whom Dr. Fenwick's appeal was addressed. The public attitude toward hospitals, the type of patients, the onerous duties of the nurses all did little to recommend nursing as a vocation or avocation to Victorian parents. But attitudes were slowly changing and applicants came forward.

The *British Whig* reported at the end of May that about fifteen applications for the Nurses Training School had been received. Miss Macarow, daughter of the late Judge, had been the first probationer accepted; Miss Margaret Hall, daughter of the Rev. Thomas Hall, had just started her course; and another candidate, Miss O'Hara of Smiths Falls, would begin June 1st. The paper said that others, for whom there was no room on the nursing staff, could attend the lectures to be given regularly by Dr. K. N. Fenwick. The Board considered letting one nurse go, as a probationer could do her work.

By October the experiment was pronounced to be entirely successful and the School was firmly established. Four probationers, under the charge of Miss Steele, late of Bellevue Hospital of New York, were becoming proficient and highly useful. Two of them served on the Hospital staff while the other two were in great demand for service in private homes. They had grey uniforms trimmed with red.

The Hospital itself had a new look; fresh paint, pictures, warmth, light, some easy chairs, bathrooms, etc. Other improvements were to come as the newly established Hospital Sunday brought donations from all the churches; that year amounting to $474. The Ladies' Committee was asked to make out a list of things which might be bought with fifty dollars from that donation. They also suggested other needs which they themselves undertook to provide: feather pillows and some new sheets. The paying public's attitude to the Hospital had changed, too. The private rooms were always full and the need for more was imminent. The Board ruled in December 1886 that the five dollars a week charged the private patients did not include luxuries or liquor. And, wondering if five dollars was a sufficient charge, they instructed the Secretary to ask Hamilton, Toronto, and Montreal hospitals how much they charged for similar accommodation.

The Hospital's new look could not hide a management problem which grew out of the expanded staff and the new Nurses' School, and was complicated by government regulations for grants and by the relationship with the Medical Faculty. Dr. Fife Fowler resigned as an Attending Medical Officer at the Hospital, saying his professional engagements and his duties in connection with the Medical College took all his time. Dr. Chamberlain Irwin was appointed to the Hospital staff in his place. Col. Duff, of the Board, and Dr. T. R. Dupuis were involved in a public dispute over the discharge of ten elderly patients no longer eligible for free beds. Dr. Dupuis was instructed to take his complaints to the Board before giving them to the press. The Attending Physicians were pressing for representation on the Board so that they could have a voice in the Board's decisions. Mr. Watson, the Steward, was complaining; his wife as Matron and Miss Steele, the Head Nurse, had constant disagreements about giving orders.

With the main problem being in the realm of authority and the chain of command, the Board of Governors decided that they really needed a man of sufficient position who could have complete authority and manage the Hospital for the Board. They advertised for a superintendent with a medical degree. Mr. and Mrs. Watson resigned; Miss Steele resigned. One Head Nurse first accepted, then refused the appointment. Miss Margaret McMillan, of the Toronto General Hospital, accepted the Board's offer of eighteen dollars a month, plus room and board, to be Head Nurse, and Matron and in charge of the Nurses' Training School. She was also informed that, 'the rules of the Hospital will be changed so as to place everyone about the institution under the authority and supervision of the Superintendent'.

Miss McMillan, having some ideas about rules and authority herself, presented a list to the Board for their approval before the Superintendent arrived. She said that the female nurses would have charge of the male as well as of the female wards. That would give the Head Nurse authority over the male nurses. She wanted the nurses to have charge of preparing and serving patients' food. This set her authority over the cook and the maids. She also listed rules for student nurses which the Board approved along with her other suggestions.

The medical Superintendent appointed by the Board was the Rev. Dr. Ephraim Hooper, a minister who had graduated in Medicine at the Royal College of Physicians and Surgeons of Kingston and hence had a degree from Queen's. Dr. Hooper's salary was to be $500 a year with a residence and board for himself, wife and two daughters. His duties would include those of the Steward and supervision and authority over the House Surgeon, Head Nurse, and all other employees. He started work on 1 May 1887, and his contract could have been terminated on three months' notice in writing from either party. He and his family were housed in the Hospital building, as Superintendents were to be for many years.

Dr. Hooper's immediate effect on the Hospital is indicated in the decisions of the Board of Governors during the first few months after his arrival. They called for tenders for bath and hot water arrangements; they bought two refrigerators, and ordered six iron wash basins. They decided to make some alterations in the first floor and to change the lying-in ward in the Watkins Wing. The new Superintendent presented further requests at almost every meeting and there were frequent meetings.

The Board decided that there was need for a formal division of their work as the Hospital demands on their time became greater. In August 1887, the first permanent Building Committee was set up to deal with maintenance, alterations, and improvements. Another committee was organized to purchase furniture and supplies – this was to become the Management Committee. That committee took over the powers and most of the duties hitherto given to the Visiting Governors.

The Attending Physicians were not given formal representation on the Board or invited to meet with the Governors. Instead they were asked to note their suggestions to the Board in a Medical Register which was to be signed each time one of them visited the Hospital, a less than subtle way of seeing how many times they did visit the Hospital. Dr. Fenwick entered suggestions in the Register as soon as it was available. 'Recommend getting two linen stretchers with poles for removing patients from the operating table. Advise purchase of Sayrs apparatus for hip joint disease, not to exceed £12.' The Board accepted some of the suggestions. The year end report, 30 September 1887, showed that almost three hundred dollars had been spent on medical and surgical appliances and instruments. The Hospital was beginning to supply more facilities with its better service.

There were still problems. In October Dr. Hooper submitted his resignation but agreed to stay on while the Board came to an agreement about a salary increase and more clearly defined rules for his guidance and duties. In March 1888, Dr. Hooper was reappointed Superintendent at $900 a year and a few months later a new set of Hospital rules went to the Lieutenant Governor for his approval. Miss McMillan's salary was increased and two more probationers were admitted to the Nurses' Training School.

The most difficult adjustments had been made, the management smoothed out for the time being, and the Nurses' Training School was a success. There was always a waiting list for admittance to the School. So, whenever one nurse finished the course or left because of illness, the Board approved the admission of another applicant. The age limit for nurses in training, originally set at eighteen to thirty-five, was changed in January 1889, to twenty-one to thirty-five. Nurses in training gave three months' service free on probation, were paid four dollars a month for the balance of the first year, and six dollars a month for the second year. They received a gratuity of twenty-five dollars, a certificate, and a silver medal on graduation. Their uniform had been changed by this time from the original grey to white with a red cross on the sleeve and a broad red belt.

Kingston General Hospital obtained its first staff specialist in September 1888, when the Board, at the request of Dr. J. C. Connell, appointed him without salary as Medical Officer to the Hospital for the Special Treatment of Diseases of the Eye and Ear. Dr. James Cameron Connell, born in 1863, received his Medical degree from Queen's and did graduate work in New York City. He was the first doctor in the Kingston area to limit his practice to the treatment of the eye, ear, nose and throat. For almost five years there had been a small section of the Hospital set aside for such special cases at the request of Dr. C. H. Lavell, a general practitioner who held the post of Professor of Ophthalmology and Oral Surgery at the Royal College, Kingston, for a few years. Dr. Connell took charge of this section.

The practice of medicine was changing, too, as new discoveries followed one another. Smallpox was sufficiently controlled by vaccination so that the smallpox hospital in the old Garratt property on King Street was closed and the building was put up for rent. But the increasing knowledge of the infectious quality of other diseases required more stringent rules and special physical arrangements in the Hospital itself. The doctors urged that a new wing be built to meet the requirements for infectious diseases. A delegation from the Board of Governors waited on the City Council to urge them to support an isolation wing. In December 1889, the Board resolved 'That a new building be erected for the Hospital to be connected with the Main Building by a covered corridor with accommodation for infectious diseases, for the Superintendent, for the Nurses and also for the laundry. The building to be erected the ensuing year and the cost not to exceed ($10,000) ten thousand dollars, including heating apparatus.'

Plans were called for immediately and a finance committee was set up to find the necessary funds. At the same Board meeting, the Management Committee (its first mention by this name) reported ordering a speaking tube with a whistle at each end to be installed from the Fever Ward to Surgery. The Committee decided that the latest and most improved inhaler should be ordered and also twenty-five 'Tait' bedsteads. Their recommendation about enlarging the operating room and installing a special gallery for the lady medical students had already been carried out.

Mrs. G. A. Kirkpatrick of the Ladies' Committee had a new scheme to raise money for improvements to the Hospital. The Ladies sponsored a series of lectures given in Convocation Hall at Queen's, on popular subjects connected with medicine. The first one, scheduled for 27 January 1890, was given by Dr. K. N. Fenwick and the title was 'Modern Dress and Tight Lacing – Exercise'. (One wonders if he talked about the exercise achieved in making the laces tight or how the tight lacing prevented healthful exercise.)

The need for the new building was urgent early in 1890. To accommodate the great number of patients, the Head Nurse gave up her room and the nurses' dining room was turned into a ward. The Board, now under the chairmanship of the Hon. G. A. Kirkpatrick after the resignation of Dr. O. S. Strange, was still considering changes in the plans for the new wing when William Nickle died in February 1890. He had been a generous benefactor of the Hospital for which, his widow intimated, there would be a considerable bequest. In April the Board accepted Mrs. Nickle's offer to give $10,000 for a building to be called the Nickle Wing. She and her heirs were granted the right of nomination to one bed in the Hospital, to be called the Nickle Bed.

The new wing on the second floor was designed to be one of the most complete for the treatment of infectious diseases. The first floor, entered by a corridor from the old Main Building, was reserved for the nurses' quarters: five bedrooms, bathroom, closets, parlour, and dining room. The front entrance to the wing, still visible today, opened into the Superintendent's private suite on the west end of the wing, five rooms completely separate from the staff.

The second floor of the Nickle Wing was entered by an outside stair at the east end, giving access to a glassed-in entry way. The floor was divided into a middle section for the nurses and around the outer section nine rooms for patients, to give a total of nineteen beds for the treatment of infectious diseases. Every room had an electric call bell, its own ventilation duct, and was designed with beveled edges and round corners to make cleaning easier. Twelve of the twenty rooms in the Wing were furnished by gifts from interested citizens.

On 2 April 1891, when the Nickle Wing was officially opened, there was evident need for it. A severe typhoid epidemic was on the decline but there were still nine cases in the General Hospital, twenty-five in the Hotel Dieu, and thirteen in homes in the city. It had been a busy winter and with more work and more staff needed for the new Wing the Board considered a request that during the winter an extra House Surgeon should be employed at the Hospital. Isaac Wood was the senior medical student serving as House Surgeon from June 1891 to June 1892. He would later join the Attending Staff to serve as assistant to Dr. Garrett in Obstetrics and Gynaecology.

In May 1891, the Board had its first formal report of trouble with the special 'Smead-Dowd' heating and ventilation system in the new Nickle Wing. This was to be only the beginning of a long series of troubles with an unsatisfactory, 'newfangled' system which ended four years later in litigation about the guarantee.

Dr. Hooper submitted his second resignation in May. A new Superintendent, Dr. Roland K. Kilborn, was appointed in June, the month that the Hospital's most famous Life Governor, Sir John A. Macdonald, died. Dr. Kilborn was a Queen's graduate in Medicine who had been in practice for twelve years in the village of Toledo, Ontario. His residence was in the Superintendent's quarters in the Nickle Wing, his office in the new board room. His duties were to oversee a Hospital with about one hundred beds, a medical staff of four Attending Physicians, one Specialist and a House Surgeon; and a Nurses' Training School with fourteen students. It was also a hospital which served as a clinical laboratory for a Medical School with one hundred and forty-five students. Perpetual hospital tickets for these Queen's medical students had been increased from ten to twelve dollars. Wages were also going up; laundress Barbara Colpick was raised from fifteen to seventeen dollars a month. The House Surgeon earned nothing but experience and the nurses were all undergraduates, except the Head Nurse whose pay was twenty dollars a month. The other untrained 'nurses' earned eight dollars a month.

There were now three Hospital buildings: one was fifty-six years old, the Watkins Wing was almost thirty, and the new Nickle Wing was having heating troubles. Some renovations and reorganization of the use of space had been made: The new board room, serving also as the Superintendent's office, had a cupboard to hold supplies and surgical instruments belonging to the Hospital. The first children's ward was being planned to take the child patients who had been scattered among the adults wherever a bed was available. The children of St. Andrew's Presbyterian Church raised money to equip this ward with twelve beds in the upper story of the Watkins Wing.

There had been expansion and change at Queen's University, too. John Carruthers Science Hall was opened in 1891 and the Queen's Medical School could then expand into the whole Medical Building. The next year Principal Grant persuaded the men of the Royal College of Physicians and Surgeons of Kingston to become once again the Medical Faculty of Queen's, although the Royal College retained its charter. The Queen's Trustees granted the use of the Medical Building to the Medical Faculty for one dollar a year, instead of the two hundred and fifty charged the Royal College. The Trustees now had a voice in the Faculty policy although the Medical Faculty was still financially dependent on the student fees. As part of the agreement, the Queen's Trustees appointed the first full-time medical professor to be paid by the University. Dr. A. P. Knight became in April 1892, Professor of Physiology, Histology, and Animal Biology in the Medical Faculty.

That same month the Board of Governors of the Kingston General Hospital, who laid down the rules for clinical lectures in the Hospital, reviewed the whole teaching situation. They decided to try restricting the number of days for clinical lectures on medicine, surgery, and gynaecology and for students going through the wards to three, instead of five, days a week. They also decided to increase by three the number of Attending Physicians; adding Doctors R. W. Garrett, H. J. Saunders, and W. G. Anglin to the staff of Doctors T. R. Dupuis, K. N. Fenwick, W. H. Henderson, and A. S. Oliver. The medical services were rearranged and Dr. Fenwick was advised to take Gynaecology as his single subject in order to give opportunity for the due employment of the newly appointed medical officers.

The Medical Staff increased, the number of patients increased. More student nurses were admitted to the Training School and had to be housed in their dining room. More accommodation was urgently needed. Dr. Fenwick proposed that a new octagonal structure be erected at the back of the Main Building to serve as an operating theatre. But the matter of priorities delayed this proposal and the Board recommended, instead, fitting up one of the private rooms as an extra operating theatre. Then the new Chairman of the Board, E. J. B. Pense, gave notice that he would recommend the erection of a separate building for housing the Superintendent and his family, the nurses, and the Maternity and Gynaecology Departments, to cost about $20,000. However, he said, the building should not be started until at least $10,000 had been raised.

Meanwhile the Board asked for estimates for finishing the attics in the Main Building and in the Nickle Wing. They also fitted up a large room in the basement of Watkins to serve as an extra maternity ward for the large number of women then coming into the Hospital for their confinements. Queen's was asked to share the expense of a new morgue and the Superintendent suggested that the old mortuary should be transformed into a nurses' dining room. A number of macabre jokes were occasioned by that change. There were other minor changes: the first laundry chute was built, hardwood replaced some soft wood floors, and cows were no longer kept on the hospital grounds.

When Miss McMillan, the Head Nurse, resigned in October 1892 to go to the Jubilee Hospital in Victoria, Miss Urquhart, who had graduated from the Nurses' Training School just a year before, applied for the job. She was appointed when the Chairman's vote broke a tie; some of the Governors felt that she was too young and inexperienced to be the Head Nurse. Miss McKay was appointed as Housekeeper, and a year later as Matron, so as to separate the latter's duties from the responsibilities of the Head Nurse. Miss Urquhart stayed only one year, resigning to marry Dr. Isaac Wood.

Ever since the Training School had been established a few of the nurses in training had been available for service in private homes in the eastern Ontario area. Most families still preferred to keep their sick ones at home and were willing to pay for trained help to assist in their care. The Hospital made a reasonable charge for this service and the nurses were in great demand. During the summer of 1892 a nurse had been supplied, free of charge, to the Orphans' Home to care for a very sick child. Chairman Pense, approving of this free service, proposed a scheme for 'Free Nursing Among the Poor'. Under that arrangement two nurses, each with at least one year's experience, were to be available, at no charge, to care for the sick poor in their own homes, a service of great importance when the mother was ill. The staff of nurses was increased to cope with this scheme which received immediate approval by the Board and by the public, some of whom made special donations to support the scheme.

The need for public support for further expansion of the Hospital facilities and services persuaded the Board to issue the first General Hospital Bulletin to be distributed to the general public. They had 1,500 copies printed to give information to the community about the facilities, staff, services, finances, and further needs of the Hospital. They pleaded for three very necessary improvements: a women's hospital, a proper laundry, and a new surgical theatre. (Unfortunately no copy of that first, 1892, Hospital Bulletin has been found. This material was taken from a report about the Bulletin published in a local newspaper.)

Chairman Pense and Principal Grant, with the approval of the Board, decided to undertake a canvass of well-to-do Kingstonians to set up a building fund for the Hospital. They were ready to start the campaign in March 1893, when the Board received notice of a substantial bequest from the estate of the late Michael Doran. Mr. Doran, head of the Kingston Foundry and Engine Works and owner of considerable real estate, had been for years contributing generously to many charities. The total bequest to the Kingston General Hospital amounted finally to about $23,000.

The Board sanctioned the expenditure of $20,000 on a Women's and Children's Hospital to be named for the donor, and called for tenders for a separate laundry. Plans were ready a month later and tenders submitted in May for the Doran Building, to be ready in January 1894. The new laundry was in operation by the fall of 1893; the old one in the basement of the Nickle Wing was remodelled to be a room for night nurses.

While the Doran Building was under way, the interior of the older buildings was renovated, and painted; many rooms were refurnished by donations. The exterior had a new plate glass door, some stained glass windows, and there was a general clean-up and landscaping of the grounds. Even the mound covering the common grave of the almost 1,400 emigrants who died in the typhus epidemic of 1847, was laid out in a garden plot and the land in front of it sodded for a lawn. His Grace Archbishop J. V. Cleary proposed to place a monument on the mound in memory of the emigrants. But some disagreement over the precise wording of the inscription delayed the dedication of the monument, the Angel of Resurrection, until 6 August 1894.

In the Hospital the last straw bed tick was discarded in 1893, after Dr. Kilborn and Miss Urquhart recommended buying twenty-four more fibre mattresses. They reported, 'They are almost indispensable as now every patient who has not a mattress sees his neighbor with one and begs for one himself.' The general diet had been improved also and so had the method of serving it; patients' meals were served on trays and a bedside table with a leaf to serve as a bed table had been designed and ordered from the Penitentiary workshops. Two more servants were hired so that convalescent patients could be sent home sooner instead of keeping them on to help with the washing of dishes, walls, and windows.

There were staff changes too. Miss Urquhart, Head Nurse, was replaced by Miss Emily MacDonell of Boston, who was given the new title of Superintendent of Nurses. Dr. Thomas M. Fenwick had been appointed to the Attending Staff in place of the late Dr. Henderson and when Dr. T. R. Dupuis died in June 1893, he was succeeded by Dr. W. G. Mundell, another Queen's graduate.

A second General Hospital Bulletin, printed for Christmas 1893, reported on the Hospital year ending September 30th. The financial report speaks for itself:

Maintenance Account of Kingston General Hospital For Year
ended September 30th 1893

RECEIPTS

From Ontario Government	$ 5,887.26
From Dominion Government	391.50
From City of Kingston Council	750.00
From County of Frontenac Council	250.00
From County of Lennox and Addington	100.00
From Village of Gananoque	20.00
From Paying Patients	3,123.87
Interest on Investments	1,095.70
Hospital Sunday Offerings	702.73
For Trained Nurses' Services	825.08
For Hospital Practice Fees	360.00
Qualifying Fees for Governors	425.00
From Garden Produce	91.35
Atkinson Estate, towards Morgue	250.00
B. W. Robertson and Misses Robertson	151.00
Misses Folger	100.00
P. R. Henderson	100.00
Legacy of Dr. W. H. Henderson	100.00
Messiah Concert	100.00
Edw. J. B. Pense	100.00
Hiram A. Calvin	75.00
Sundry Donations	460.87
Sundry Donations for District Nursing	99.00
	$15,558.36

EXPENDITURES

Meat	$ 1,144.70
Butter	741.22
Bread, Flour, etc.	493.01
Milk	584.98
Tea and Coffee	243.73
Vegetables	364.51
Groceries	1,439.03
Medicines	806.66
Medical and Surgical Appliances	598.58
Furniture, Bedding, Hardware, etc.	1,118.93
Brooms, Brushes and Soap	184.06
Fuel	1,320.20

Light	433.54
Water	78.56
Salaries and Wages	3,647.49
Insurance	209.00
Contingencies	1,036.74
Printing and Stationery	108.88
Repairs, ordinary	1,055.59
	$15,609.41

The Bulletin also had articles on the benefits of hospital treatment, the need for a home for incurables, and the virtue of giving. There was a passionate appeal signed Fidelis (*nom de plume* of Agnes Maule Machar) for volunteer visitors to bring cheer to the charity patients. More factual reports told of progress on the new Doran Building and listed other recent improvements. A brief story about the Nurses' Training School said there was no danger of the supply of trained nurses exceeding the demand. And a member of the nursing staff appealed for a new Nurses' Home to house the nineteen nurses in training.

The Doran Building was officially opened on 26 February 1894, by the Hon. G. A. Kirkpatrick, Lieutenant Governor of Ontario. This women's hospital was a model of its kind – light, airy, well ventilated; with separate wards for maternity cases, for women's diseases and for isolation. The five private rooms, each with a gas grate, were to cost ten dollars a week. The operating room, with 'an ante room for etherizing', was furnished with the latest equipment; an operating table and other furnishings all in iron and glass, instead of the usual wood ones. Dr. K. N. Fenwick said that twenty years before there would have been no use for an operating room in a women's hospital – 'no such work was done then'. There were laboratories, pantries and special rooms for the surgeons and for the Doran Head Nurse, a Miss Fraser who was paid ten dollars a month. The building had its own coal furnace and the light fittings were for gas and electricity; the electric lights, however, were not to be used except for operations or examinations.

Provision of hot meals for the patients in Doran was a problem from the beginning since the only Hospital kitchen was in the basement of the old Main Building. It was soon discovered that to carry food across to the Doran Building was not satisfactory at any time of year, even after covered containers were provided. An enclosed corridor between the buildings or a kitchen in Doran had to be considered before the next winter. But hot food was not the only difficulty. The separate building also caused staff problems with nurses and with maids. Dr. K. N. Fenwick, whose 1888 textbook on Obstetrics emphasized isolation and cleanliness, took issue with the staffing arrangements in Doran. He said that to guard his patients from infection, the nurses and a maid serving in Doran should be limited to that one building and not have daily contact with the other wards. And, he said, if there were not enough nurses to do that the Governors should call in some of the nurses who were out on duty in private homes.

The management of a Hospital with almost one hundred and fifty beds brought problems in coordination and communication. The old rules and regulations often did not fit current situations and it was sometimes easier to blame others than to accept responsibility. The Medical Staff was growing increasingly impatient with the lack of proper facilities and wanted a stronger voice in decisions regarding priorities in major expenditures. The Chairman of the Board resigned after a disagreement about policy. The Medical Superintendent and the Superintendent of Nurses were not in accord and appealed to the Board to settle the argument. Various Attending Physicians asked for more and better equipment, and urged the provision of a proper operating theatre in the Main Building. They recommended, among other things, that there should be a standard admission card for patients. The Governors thought that the Medical Staff should be called together to decide which request had priority and to consult with and advise the Superintendent, especially on economies.

Eight doctors met on Friday, 30 November 1894, to organize the first Medical Board of the Kingston General Hospital. Dr. A. S. Oliver was elected Chairman, Dr. Kilborn, the Superintendent of the Hospital, was elected Secretary. The minutes of that first meeting are very brief: a motion that 'the services of the Medical and Surgical men and Specialists continue as at present' was carried. They had a discussion on the methods of prescribing and agreed to prepare a list of drugs, and to use, in so far as it was possible, the drugs on hand. They agreed to caution the House Surgeons on the indiscriminate use of morphine and whiskey.

The next time the Medical Board had a quorum was in March 1895, when they met, at the request of the Board of Governors, to consider the plans for a new surgical amphitheatre. Dr. K. N. Fenwick offered to give $2,500 so that the theatre he had proposed three years before could be built. His offer was accepted and when the tenders were for almost $4,000 the Governors decided to pay the difference but to name the room after Dr. Fenwick. Dr. A. P. Chown offered to provide all the glassware and Dr. Garrett added to a grant from the Dr. Henderson estate to buy an 'Endibohls' operating table to go in the new operating theatre.

On 15 October 1895, the formal opening of the 1895–1896 session of the Queen's Medical Faculty and Dr. Fenwick's presentation of his gift to the Hospital took place in the new Fenwick Operating Theatre, known thereafter as the F.O.T. It was a two storey, semicircular, stone building attached to the back of the Main Building, just east of the entrance. The room on the lower level served as a waiting room for students and was connected by a stair to the amphitheatre. On the main floor three rows of seats for one hundred students were arranged in a semicircle, the walls, seats, and rails all painted white. The operating 'arena' had a slate floor, walls of polished white marble, and the ground glass ceiling diffused the light from a large skylight in the roof. Ten windows set high in the walls added to the illumination. There were sets of wash basins on each side, three glass tables, and a boiler to sterilize water. The new Endibohls operating table was equipped with a Morris extension.

Pride in this new facility was tempered by the report the Board had just received of the financial operation of the Hospital to September 30th. For the past two years expenses had exceeded income by nearly $2,800 a year. Another deficit of $2,679.15 in a total operation of about $16,000 was, to say the least, alarming. Since the capital fund – in addition to the Nickle and Doran legacies and the Fenwick gift – had been expended on building, there was no interest income, only higher maintenance costs. The Board, deciding that extreme economy had to be instituted immediately, set up a special committee to consider how to increase the income and lessen the expenditure. The committee brought in fifteen recommendations to a special meeting of the Board six days after the F.O.T. was formally opened.

As a result, when Miss MacDonnell resigned, she was replaced by Miss Helena MacMillan to be both Superintendent of Nurses and Housekeeper; the two jobs which had been separated only three years before. Yet in a one hundred and fifty bed Hospital the combined jobs were too much for one person. Miss MacMillan soon offered to accept $100 less a year if she could have an assistant and one was promptly appointed. The other recommendations for cutting expenses required further consideration and consultation with the Superintendent, with the Medical Board, and with Queen's University.

But the plans for increasing the income were implemented immediately. The provincial, municipal, and county governments were approached for increased grants. Queen's was asked to pay $250 a year for the use of Hospital lecture and clinical facilities. The subscription Governors were all reminded to pay their annual fee of four dollars and the minimum charge for a private room was set at seven dollars a week.

There were also to be special economies in the operation of the Hospital: a single dining room had to serve the Superintendent and his family, the House Surgeons, the Superintendent of Nurses, and all the nurses. Only candles were to be used after eight p.m. The Superintendent was instructed to submit weekly, detailed financial statements to the Board. The committee also recommended that the graduate nurse in the Doran Building be given three months' notice, and that the nurses in training not be paid after September 1896. They said that one medical graduate at no salary should replace the two undergraduate House Surgeons (a saving on board, room, and laundry), and that the Medical Superintendent's salary should be reduced by $100 to $900.

The penny-pinching and constant scrutiny of expenditures were bad enough, but a cut in salary was too much. Dr. Kilborn submitted his resignation in January 1896, saying that although he had been given excellent cooperation he felt that his position had 'not been as cordially acceptable as in former years'. He asked to be relieved at the earliest convenience so that he might engage in private practice. The Board commended his work, accepted his resignation and decided to advertise for a new Medical Superintendent at $600 a year. Fifty-eight men applied for the job. On 17 February 1896, the Board appointed Dr. James Third of Trenton, a Queen's graduate, to become Superintendent of the Kingston Hospital in June.

Over a few months there had been major changes in the Attending Medical Staff of the Hospital. On 2 December 1895, on motion of Dr. H. J. Saunders, seconded by Dr. Fenwick, the Board approved the appointment of Dr. Walter T. Connell as Pathologist to the Hospital. Dr. Connell, a Queen's graduate of 1894, had been invited, while he was studying in England, to return to Queen's as Professor of Pathology and Bacteriology. He became the second full-time medical professor to be appointed by the University and he was to serve Queen's and the Kingston General Hospital with distinction and devotion until his retirement in 1943.

Another staff change came as the result of the tragic death from blood poisoning of Dr. K. N. Fenwick. A small scratch on his left hand, of which he was unaware, became infected after he performed an operation to remove an abscess, which ruptured during the operation. (The rubber gloves lately introduced in operative surgery were first used to protect the hands of the person in charge of the instruments, not the surgeon, from the effects of carbolic acid solution.) Although Dr. Fenwick washed his hands immediately, within a few days he was seriously ill. Dr. Garrett and Dr. Anglin did everything possible for him, to no avail. Dr. Thomas Roddick of Montreal was telegraphed for and a special train brought him to Kingston. He could do nothing but advise them to ease the pain. On the evening of 21 January 1896 Dr. Fenwick died at his residence on King Street. Queen's University lost a Professor of Obstetrics and Gynaecology, Kingston General Hospital lost a Life Governor and a member of its Attending Staff, Head of the Department of Gynaecology. The medical profession lost a brilliant and dedicated colleague.

Within a month Dr. Herbert J. Saunders, another member of the Attending Staff, was dead and Dr. David Cunningham (Queen's 1890) took his place at the Hospital. Dr. Fenwick's duties at Queen's and at the Hospital were taken on by Dr. Garrett. Dr. John Herald (Queen's 1884) took Fenwick's place on the Attending Staff and Mr. W. F. Nickle was appointed a Life Governor to fill Fenwick's place on the Board of Governors. But the work Dr. Fenwick had been doing in gynaecology was too much when added to Dr. Garrett's teaching, hospital work and private practice; he needed help. In April Dr. Isaac Wood was appointed as his assistant at Queen's and at the Hospital to provide adequate care for the increasing number of patients who were coming to the women's hospital.

There were also many more patients in the isolation section of the Nickle Wing. That year (1896), with twenty-five to thirty cases of typhoid at a time, other wards had to be set aside for their care, and additional strains were put on the nursing staff. One nurse died and three others were seriously ill with the disease. Tests and vaccination for typhoid were discovered that year but were not yet available in Canada. The Kingston Board of Health, attempting to remove a possible source of infection, recommended flushing out some offensive drains and replacing old stone ones with the newer tile drains. The fear of further epidemics moved public officials to plan other sanitary reforms. Yet the very next year there was a serious outbreak of diphtheria in Kingston, although diphtheria serum was then available. The latest treatment for diphtheria, however, made it possible for the Kingston General Hospital to report that of one hundred patients with the disease there had been no deaths.

The doctors in Kingston were taking prompt advantage of the latest discoveries, sometimes with the help of scientists at the University. In December 1895, Roentgen had announced the discovery of X-ray. In May 1896, Captain Cochrane at John Carruthers Science Hall at Queen's used the X-ray machine he had built to locate a needle in a woman's hand. A twelve-minute exposure was used for each of the two plates made, which revealed the needle and enabled Dr. Kilborn to extract it successfully.

Dr. James Third arrived in June to take over his duties as Medical Superintendent. Greatly excited by the implications of X-ray, he persuaded the Board to acquire the materials so that one could be built for the Hospital. Although Dr. Third was quickly convinced of its value as a diagnostic agent he was slower to recommend it in therapy. He became a strong advocate of X-ray in diagnosing tubercular lesions in the lung when auscultation and percussion indicated no departure from the normal. While he was Superintendent of the Hospital he was in charge of, and made good use of, the X-ray machine. By some experimental work he also improved the fluoroscope then available and exhibited its work at a meeting of the Kingston Medical and Surgical Society.

The annual report of the Kingston General Hospital, as of 30 September 1896, showed improvement in the financial situation. The City of Kingston grant had been increased to $1,000 and there had been a saving of $870 in salaries and household expenses. The Board of Governors complimented Superintendent Third who had 'discovered and stopped leaks in the expenses', and Superintendent of Nurses Miss MacMillan who had surmounted the many difficulties with sick nurses during the typhoid epidemic. They noted that 'the machinery of the Hospital is running without friction or trouble of any kind'. The staff at that time included nine Attending Physicians, the two Superintendents, a Housekeeper, two House Surgeons, twenty nurses, and twelve servants.

The Board also noted with interest the first issue of the *Kingston Medical Quarterly*, October 1896, edited by Dr. John Herald. One section, called 'Hospital Notes', had In Memoriams for Dr. Fenwick, Dr. Saunders, Dr. D. C. Hickey and Dr. Annie Dickson, daughter of the late Dr. J. R. Dickson and one of the early women graduates of medicine in Ontario. The publication was issued quarterly for the next thirteen years; the name changed in 1903 to *Queen's Medical Quarterly*. The articles were mostly by Kingston doctors covering the Medical Faculty, the General Hospital, case reports, and reports of medical discoveries at home and abroad. The reports of the Kingston Medical and Surgical Society are especially interesting, showing that, through the cooperation of Queen's and the Hospital, continuing education was offered to the medical profession in the area. The November 1899 annual meeting of the Society was open to all Kingston doctors, and twelve attended from outside Kingston. The morning session was devoted to observing operations, the afternoon to special clinics, including one at Rockwood Hospital. In the evening there were talks on new discoveries and new techniques in medicine.

The new treatments generally required more and better trained personnel to administer them. On the strong recommendation of the Attending Staff the Board decided in 1897 to appoint as House Surgeons two graduates, instead of the usual two final year students, recommended by the Medical Faculty. Dr. G. W. Mylks and Dr. Croskery were the first two graduates appointed.

The doctors wanted better qualified help also in other positions. They asked that the assistant to the Superintendent of Nurses be placed in charge of the operating room and that a senior nurse be put in charge of the night nurses, who were all juniors. The Superintendent of Nurses proposed to recognize the achievements of her nurses in training by permitting the use of a black band on the caps of nurses who received more than sixty per cent on their junior examinations. It was the highest honour available and might be removed for misconduct or poor work.

Graduates of the Nurses' Training School, living in Kingston, formed a society to undertake as their first project, the improvement of the nurses' accommodation at the Hospital. Being highly practical, they decided to back their requests to the Board with money and in July 1897, held a garden party to start their building fund. Mrs. Beamish, President of the Nurses Alumnae, accompanied some of the Governors on an inspection of the nurses' quarters and made some suggestions. She said that the main trouble was that the nurses' rooms were so scattered about the Hospital that proper superintendence was very difficult. The Alumnae wanted agreement on a long range plan which would achieve a separate nurses' home.

In November Miss MacMillan resigned and Miss Alice Taylor of Toronto, was selected from the twenty-three applicants to be the new Superintendent of Nurses. She disapproved of the common dining hall, and asked for some changes in staff dining arrangements. The Board's decision that 'in the interests of discipline there should be a separate dining room for the Lady Superintendent and the House Surgeons' was not popular with either the nurses or the young House Surgeons. However, authority had to be maintained and familiarity discouraged. There had been an occasion when one nurse, speaking disrespectfully to the Superintendent of Nurses, had been denied her diploma until she apologized.

Strict economy had been so effective that the annual report showed a loss on the year's operation of the Hospital of only $163. At last the installation of an elevator, which had long been urgently requested by all the staff, could be considered. Dr. Third's salary was increased to $1,000 a year and the Board decided that future bequests should be deposited in a capital fund account. However, the Board felt that caution was still necessary. Dr. Herald's suggestion that three, instead of two, House Surgeons should be appointed was deferred. But the Board approved the request of the Flower Circle to have a Christmas tree for the patients set up in the Fenwick Operating Theatre.

Then disaster struck. Friday morning, 24 December 1897, flames broke out in the kitchen of St. George's Ward, at the east end of the upper storey of the Main Building. Orderly Cole, melting beeswax in turpentine to polish the kitchen floor, spilled some on the flames. Doors were closed, help was called. Dr. Herald used the Babcock extinguisher but could not put out the fire. Canvas hose was rushed over from Doran but the outside fire hydrants were frozen. Before they could be thawed the flames had spread to the roof of the Watkins Wing and patients had to be evacuated.

Doctors, nurses, servants and neighbours helped to move the patients. The seven sick children in St. Andrew's Ward, on the top floor of the Watkins Wing, were quickly bundled up and carriages and wagons were commandeered to take them to the Orphans' Home on Union Street. The other forty patients in the Watkins Wing and the Main Building were moved into the Doran Building and the Nickle Wing for temporary shelter. A few patients were taken to the Richardsons' houses next to the Hospital. There was an immediate offer of accommodation from Hotel Dieu and from Queen's University. Kingston offered the use of Ontario Hall in the City Building and, among many others, Archbishop Lewis offered the use of his residence.

Firemen, soldiers, and citizens fought the flames. Volunteers managed to move furniture and equipment out of the Main Building but the content of the Watkins Wing was almost a total loss. A line of about forty men passed pails of water from hand to hand up many flights of stairs to saturate the rooms and corridors of the

Main Building, and managed to save it from little more than water damage. Only a small part of its roof, next to the Watkins Wing, was burned. In about two hours the fire was out; the twisted and blackened ruins of the Watkins Wing froze quickly in the December air.

The Board of Governors, meeting in emergency session in the Doran Building, resolved that the fire being under control, they would engage at once sufficient help to close in the roof and broken windows of the Main Building. Within a week some patients were back in the western section of the Main Building and the damage claims had been submitted. Insurance covered damages for $5,388 to Watkins, $858 to Main and $1,222 to furniture and equipment. There were immediate and generous offers of financial help from Kingstonians.

The Watkins Wing Building Committee appointed William Newlands as architect and went into emergency sessions. A month later the Board approved plans for the reconstruction of the Watkins Wing including a third storey, estimated to cost $6,500 plus the insurance award. Within another month tenders had been accepted totalling $9,228, the building to be completed by July 1898. Furniture and equipment would be extra. The plans, completed in such a rush, were constantly modified over the next few months. The Board authorized the addition of electric wiring, increased the size of the water main and provided for the installation of a proper fire escape and of a new and larger heating unit. But they could not include the badly needed elevator; the available funds were insufficient.

The Board resolved to ask for estimates for fitting up the attic of the Main Building for consumptive patients. The Visiting Governors inspected the space and advised against it although they recognized the need for separate and increased space for the treatment of tuberculosis. In view of the recent fire they considered that adequate fire protection for Main and for Nickle should have priority and should certainly precede increased use of any attic space.

The rebuilt Watkins Wing was isolated by fire doors from the Main Building and connected to Doran by a basement passage. It had two floors of private rooms, smaller than the old ones had been so the number could be increased. The new third floor had three semi-private wards on the north side and, on the south side (the children's section), a room for boys and one for girls, separated by a recreation room with a glassed-in balcony. The Board publicly thanked the many donors for the gifts to furnish the wing. The gifts included, in many cases, complete furnishings for a private room even to special sheets, blankets, china, and silverware.

With the Watkins Wing back in operation, including the new third floor, Hospital accommodation had increased to one hundred and sixty-eight beds, and services had to be available for a greater number of private patients. The Board received requests for an extra orderly, an increase in the nursing staff from twenty to twenty-two, and a third House Surgeon. There was certainly enough work to warrant the increase but the problem of sufficient staff accommodation could be resolved only by crowding the present staff. That crowding was already causing problems in the Nurses' Training School. Miss Taylor then resigned, to be succeeded by Miss Elizabeth Flaws.

In spite of all the changes which had taken place at the Hospital, the financial records had been continued in the same way since the first incorporation. Mr. J. E. Clark, who for twenty-three years had served as Secretary-Treasurer of the Board of Governors, kept some of the records in his office downtown and the Superintendent had some in his office in the Hospital. On Mr. Clark's resignation the Management Committee recommended that a new set of books should be opened, all kept at the Hospital, and that 'a lady be employed as a stenographer and typewriter and to keep the account books of the Hospital'. Dr. Third, the Superintendent, was appointed Treasurer. In September 1899, Miss Emma Hunter was appointed Stenographer and Bookkeeper at $14 a month. No one, seeing the neat young lady at a table in the corner of the waiting room, could possibly have had any idea of what Emma Hunter was to mean to the running of the Kingston General Hospital over the fifty-eight years she served it so well. In the years following, no one had a more encyclopaedic knowledge of every aspect of the management of the Hospital or served it with more single-minded devotion than Emma Hunter.

The year 1899 closed with the Board of Governors expressing a cautious note of optimism about the affairs of the Hospital. The grant from the City of Kingston had increased in ten years from $500 to $1,500; and the yearly deficit was under $300. The number of paying patients was steadily increasing and expenses were under control. The Hospital buildings were in good condition, the only problem being the Smead-Dowd heating and ventilation system in the Nickle Wing. And although the Medical Board was dissatisfied with the arrangement for the isolation of infectious diseases, changes were being considered to meet some of their recommendations.

The Board authorized the publication of the annual report for 1899 and decided that it should include a picture of the exterior of the Hospital and three pictures of the interior. On December 16th the Governors met to go in a body to the funeral of Sir George Airey Kirkpatrick, late Lieutenant Governor of Ontario and former Chairman of the Board of Governors of the Kingston General Hospital.

Six

The turn of the century was a time to take stock of accomplishments and to look to *The New* the future. The country was prosperous and a new national pride was evident under *Century and* Prime Minister Laurier's government; yet the ties with Britain were still strong. A *World War I* second Canadian contingent was on its way to the Boer War, and city bells and *1900–1918* whistles would soon announce the relief of Ladysmith and later, the relief of Mafeking. There was a surge of migration to the west and, in the east, improved working conditions encouraged the movement of the younger rural population to the cities.

James A. Minnes, mayor of Kingston, a city of about 18,000, took pride in a big government drydock recently built for $800,000. Factories in the city, making locomotives, steam engines, agricultural equipment, pianos, cigars, cotton textiles, and hosiery, provided steady employment for a growing population. The city business directory included, among others, the names of seven carriage and wagon makers, five cabinet makers, three electricians, three corset makers and ninety-four dress-makers. For those who could afford it, help was plentiful; a domestic help registry brought girls from the country to help in many city homes. Times were prosperous; the rate of taxation in Kingston was eighteen and a half mills.

Two rail lines and a number of stage routes served Kingston; in season, steamboats called daily at her docks. The Kingston street railway had discarded the last of the horse-drawn cars in favour of electric ones. But the livery stables still did a good business and many families had their own horses and carriages housed in outbuildings behind their homes.

Education was then, as now, an important industry. Kingston children attended eight public and three separate schools, a collegiate, two convents and six private schools. Queen's University, rapidly expanding, had about eight hundred students from across the country in its four permanent and two frame buildings. Principal George M. Grant, who had travelled throughout Canada in his drive for funds for Queen's, received solid provincial support, in 1900, with a grant of $112,500. The City of Kingston also made a grant and within four years there were four new buildings on the campus.

Queen's Medical Faculty had three full-time professors paid by the University but the part-time professors were still dependent on student fees. Dr. Fife Fowler, venerable President of the Medical Faculty, retained control of policy until his death in October 1903; then Queen's took over. Dr. Michael Sullivan, who had been the first Kingston student to enter the Medical School and who was a strong supporter of its separate status as the Royal College of Physicians and Surgeons of Kingston, handed in his resignation. In 1904, he reluctantly gave the charter, seal, and book of the Royal College to the new Dean of the Medical Faculty, Dr. J. C. Connell. Dean Connell's campaign to have Queen's take more responsibility for expenses as well as policy was not completely successful until 1913. When the Trustees assumed complete financial responsibility for the Medical Faculty, it was receiving an annual provincial grant of $11,000.

Three daily papers brought news of the world to a population largely conservative; the moderately wealthy families, the professional, official, and military were still predominant in city affairs. Kingston, according to the City Directory of 1899, was the most charitable city of its size on the continent, with two hospitals, two orphans' homes, and two homes for adults, all supported chiefly by donations. However, the directors of the various institutions had reservations about how well they were supported by these donations and continued their efforts to secure dependable and adequate government support for the charities.

Kingston at the turn of the century had over twenty-five doctors, the majority of them connected with Queen's Medical Faculty and either the Hotel Dieu or the Kingston General Hospital. At the first annual meeting of the Kingston Medical and Surgical Society, the president, Dr. John Herald, reviewed the progress of medicine. He noted that blistering and blood-letting were very rare and that strong emetics and physic were more rationally used. The chemist, pathologist, and bacteriologist had come to the aid of the physician, and new instruments had also been of great help in the more accurate diagnosis of disease. Treatment of disease, he said, had been improved by hypodermic medication, the use of antiseptics and anaesthetics, regulation of diet, the transfusion of blood and saline solution, and by serum therapy.

The medical profession had interested itself in sanitary reforms to prevent the spread of disease and this, Dr. Herald said, was its most important task. He cited measures concerning ventilation, disposal of garbage and sewage, clean water supplies, isolation and immunization as health precautions taken under the pressure of medical opinion.

Looking at what should be done in the future, Dr. Herald urged the pathologist and bacteriologist to search for the causes of disease so that causes, rather than symptoms, could be treated. Yet, he added, much remained to be done in the realm of prophylaxis, and he dealt briefly with the problems surrounding the treatment of tuberculosis and the need to convince the public that it was, to a large extent, a preventable disease.

Research projects were already under way in Kingston. Dr. Walter T. Connell, Pathologist to the Kingston General Hospital and Professor of Pathology and Bacteriology at Queen's, was engaged in research from the time of his appointment in 1895. His 1897 report on dairy bacteriology had already proved of great practical benefit and commercial value to the cheese industry. His continuing work in clinical bacteriology led the Ontario government to establish a Public Health Laboratory in Kingston in 1904 and place him in charge of it. It was also mainly his work which brought a government grant to Queen's in 1905, to build a new medical building which would house the work in pathology and bacteriology.

In 1900, the Governors of the Kingston General Hospital, E. H. Smythe, chairman, were considering a recommendation to alter the Nickle Wing to secure better isolation for infectious diseases and, it was hoped, to give better accommodation for the twenty-five student nurses. At one point in the discussions, which continued for about three years, the Governors suggested that the Nickle Wing become a nurses' home and that a separate building be provided for infectious diseases. The Nickle family objected to any change in the use of the Wing which they had given specifically as an isolation building. Their desires were dramatically supported when a severe typhoid epidemic in the first four months of 1903 filled both the hospitals and resulted in fourteen deaths. In May 1903, the Board decided to alter Nickle to double the accommodation for infectious diseases. They would build a separate nurses' home. The next month the Nickle Wing was vacated and turned over to the contractor to be finished early in 1904.

The Hospital in February 1900, had lost one of its devoted staff members when Dr. Alfred Sales Oliver died after a very brief illness. A protégé of Dr. James Sampson, he had been associated with the Hospital since his term as House Surgeon in 1860 and had served for over a quarter of a century also as Surgeon to the Kingston Gaol. There were immediate applications to fill the vacant place on the Hospital Medical Staff. A former chairman of the Board asked that his son be appointed; a former superintendent applied also. The Medical Staff, already incensed by controversy over proposed changes in the Nickle Wing, wanted to exert more control over membership on the attending staff and opted for a delaying action. They asked that no new appointment be made to fill Dr. Oliver's place until various staff duties could be rearranged for the Medical Superintendent, and for the thirteen doctors and three House Surgeons.

In 1900, after a hiatus of three years, the Medical Staff held very frequent meetings to consider the plans for the alteration of the Nickle Wing and to deal with recommendations about staff appointments. They asked that two doctors on staff be appointed as anaesthetists – Dr. G. W. Mylks for the Doran Building and Dr. John Herald for the rest of the Hospital, to serve without pay. Up to this time the Medical Superintendent was supposed to give all anaesthetics but actually any doctor or House Surgeon available had been called on when needed.

There was also a problem about the control of the X-ray machine. When Dr. Third resigned in July 1900, he was replaced as Medical Superintendent and Treasurer by Dr. Andrew Haig of Campbellford. The Medical Staff recommended that Dr. Third should continue to have charge of the X-ray and be named Radiographer; but since Dr. Kilborn had been appointed in Dr. Oliver's place there was no opening on the Attending Staff for Dr. Third until after the death of Dr. Thomas Fenwick in December 1900. So, from the time Dr. Haig was appointed Superintendent in July, he was in charge of the machine and continued to be even after Dr. Third joined the staff. In May 1901, it was reported to the Management Committee that the X-ray machine was out of repair and had been for some time. Management suggested a conference with Dr. Third who had instituted the X-ray work at the Hospital. A month later the X-ray was reported to be in good working order with Dr. Third again in charge of it.

As the public wards were not being used to capacity, the Board of Governors, late in 1900, proposed to the Medical Staff that the wards of the Hospital be thrown open to practising physicians generally. The Medical Staff replied that any change in ward attendance would not be in the best interests of the Kingston General Hospital. They suggested that the number of ward patients might be increased if the meals were improved. However, in spite of this advice, the Governors of the Hospital changed the regulations so that any practitioner could attend a patient in a public ward and patients so attended were not to be available for clinical instruction. The Queen's Medical Faculty and the Medical Staff at the Hospital were extremely upset by this ruling which cut down the already limited amount of clinical material for the expanding medical school. They suggested that the quality of medical teaching at Queen's and the quality of medical treatment at the Hospital were mutually dependent and that it might be well for the Governors to compare the Kingston General Hospital to a hospital in a city which did not have a medical school.

The use of the Hospital, not only by the medical students but also by the public, especially the paying public, had greatly increased. In 1900, 1,335 patients were admitted and 1,150 others were treated in the out-patient department. Changed social conditions and changed attitudes toward health had some influence on the numbers admitted. But the biggest influence was the increased and skilled service in both nursing care, and in medicine and surgery offered by the Hospital. Some minor surgery was still done in the doctors' offices but most of the surgery was confined to the Hospital which could provide the necessary equipment and skilled assistance needed in new procedures.

Dr. R. W. Garrett, in a 1900 issue of the *Kingston Medical Quarterly*, wrote about 'Modern Aseptic Surgical Technique in Kingston General Hospital'. He outlined the preparation of the surgeon and assistants, noting the use of a long operating gown (sterilized); the hands and arms were to be scrubbed for ten minutes with green soap and a sterile brush, then to be immersed successively in a saturated solution of permanganate of potash, of oxalic acid, in sterile water, in bichloride and finally washed off in sterile water or a salt solution. (Rubber gloves first used in England in 1891 were evidently not yet used at the Hospital.) The instruments were to be boiled ten minutes and plain sterilized or iodoform gauze was to be used as sponges attached to ten inch tapes.

Surgeons at the Hospital, in the fall of 1900, had been given permission to remove some marble slabs from the wall of the Fenwick Operating Theatre to install a new set of sterilizers, at their own expense. Dr. Isaac Wood presented a new operating table for the Doran Building at a cost of $88. (The duty on it which amounted to $26.40, the Board agreed to pay.) With these improvements in facilities the Governors decided to charge two dollars for the use of the operating room, for all those who were able to pay. They decided also that the use of the operating rooms, especially of the F.O.T., for purposes other than operations had to be discouraged. The Flower Circle had to find another place for its Christmas tree. The Board wrote to the secretary of the Medical Faculty of Queen's, in 1902, 'to ascertain whether some of the clinical lectures, now delivered in the operating amphitheatre in the morning, could not be given in the afternoon, as considerable inconvenience was felt by the medical men who needed the theatre in the morning for surgical operations'. For lectures they recommended the use of the students' waiting room, below the operating theatre.

The Board had another suggestion for Queen's students in connection with the Hospital's regular search for funds – a proposal for hospital insurance. The Queen's Alma Mater Society, in December 1901, set up a committee to discuss the proposed arrangement that for one dollar a year a student would be assured the advantages of a private room at the Kingston General Hospital if 250 students signed up for the plan. The students accepted the proposal immediately, asking that it be put into effect for the second half of the school year, 7 January to 1 May 1902, for fifty cents a student. D. M. Solandt, chairman of the student committee to get sub-scribers, reported that in the first week of January 240 had already signed and that others wishing to do so would have to subscribe at once. This hospital insurance scheme was continued for many years; in 1908 they sold 508 student tickets; ten years later the Queen's Senate considered making the insurance compulsory.

After a particularly difficult winter and spring of 1902 when a number of her nurses had been ill with typhoid, Miss Flaws, Superintendent of Nurses, sent a request to the Management Committee. She asked that she be allowed to increase the nursing staff, all student nurses, from twenty-seven to thirty-five and to appoint three graduate nurses as Supervisors. Management agreed that the increase was needed, but when they faced her with the question of accommodation for this extra staff Miss Flaws had no solution. A delegation of nurses had already met the Management Committee to urge them to provide a home for the nurses and the Committee decided to look for a nearby house which might be rented for temporary quarters.

Queen's Trustees offered to the Hospital the temporary use of the centre section of Summerhill House on the Queen's campus as accommodation for the nurses in October 1902; the rent to be fifteen dollars a month. Principal Grant had died in May and his successor, Principal Daniel Gordon, would not bring his family to Kingston for about a year. So on November 5th Mrs. Martin and fourteen nurses moved into Summerhill. They moved again the next spring to another temporary residence, St. Lawrence Cottage, the Herchmer house on King Street (on the site of the present Faculty Club). That was much better accommodation than some of the other nurses had, since during the renovation of the Nickle Wing, the nurses who had occupied rooms there were moved to the attics of Watkins and Doran. The new Nurses' Residence, opened in May 1904, provided welcome, convenient, and, for some time, sufficient accommodation for the nurses at the Kingston General Hospital.

Meantime various improvements had been made in the rest of the Hospital. The elevator which had been needed and considered for so long, was installed in 1901. It was driven by water pressure, would not raise the required weight, and generally did not work as promised. Various parts were replaced and, when it was repaired, inspected, and under guarantee, the King's Daughters and Sons and a representative of the Nicol Estate made a formal presentation of it as their gift to the Hospital. The Governors hired a man to operate it, and decided that the elevator should not run after 6:30 p.m. but that arrangements would be made for its use in emergency cases. Unfortunately, the elevator continued to give trouble until the complete works were replaced in 1904.

Mechanical problems with elevators and telephones and maintenance problems with plumbing and painting were more easily solved than the management problems with workers and the demands of the Medical Staff. There was a fairly frequent turnover of help, for it was very difficult to get and keep housekeepers and cooks who could cope efficiently and economically with their duties. The one office worker, Emma Hunter, gave great satisfaction and dealt with an increasing number of jobs, large and small.

Doctors, keeping up with advances in medical knowledge, techniques, and equipment, asked for more space and better facilities. They had, however, very practical suggestions for the Governors and, contributing from their own funds, encouraged gifts from friends of the Hospital. In April 1903, the Governors were invited to inspect a gift from the Misses Robertson, 'a new apparatus for the electrical treatment of nervous disorders', fitted up in the anteroom of the F.O.T. There was some discussion about setting aside a private room for 'nervous patients' for the treatment of 'an ever increasing chain of disorders that for want of a better name we term neuroses'. A room in the basement was fitted up later.

Doctors on staff at the Hospital seldom felt the need for any formal staff meeting so long as they could get what they wanted by individual effort. They had made their recommendations regarding the renovation of the Nickle Wing in 1900; but three years later the plans were still not complete. Staff Doctors Herald, J. C. Connell, Garrett, Kilborn, Anglin, Mylks, Mundell, and Wood met to reorganize the old Medical Board as the Medical Staff of the Kingston General Hospital. They asked that two members of the Medical Staff serve henceforth on the Management Committee and the minutes of that committee indicate that Medical Staff approval was requested thereafter for Management decisions which might affect the doctors.

The Medical Staff exerted sufficient pressure to get the Nickle Wing renovated, in 1903, to make it a safe and satisfactory isolation hospital. They then took steps to have the various services conform to proper isolation practices. They asked that all the cooking for isolation be done, not in the main kitchen, but in the Nickle Wing. They directed that there be no movement of nurses between isolation and the rest of the Hospital and took similar measures for the House Surgeons.

The work of the three House Surgeons was subdivided; they were each to be assigned to special departments for a certain number of months. Thus the House Surgeon on duty in the Infectious and Pathological service would not do any Medical or Surgical service until he was assigned to them. The staff was anxious to institute whatever restrictions were necessary in order to avoid another epidemic like the typhoid siege they had just been through.

The doctors had also been asking for more facilities for surgery. Just opposite the F.O.T., the surgeons found space for an extra operating room which was not to be available for medical lectures or entertainments by the Flower Circle. They offered to pay the cost themselves of fitting up this House Surgeons' room for a new surgery. A makeshift solution, it was gas lit, and had no electricity for over a year when a thirty-two candle-power light was installed 'for use on dark days and nights'. This room was named the Louise Operating Room, known as the L.O.R., in honour of Princess Louise.

A crisis in management came with the resignation of Dr. Haig as Superintendent in August of 1903. As the attractions of private practice were making it difficult to get and keep medical superintendents, it was thought well to consider possible alternatives. Professor John Marshall, Chairman of the Board of Governors, made a report on the advantages and disadvantages of having a medical or a lay superintendent, citing the necessary changes in administration if a lay appointment were made. Within a month the Board had agreed to hire a lay superintendent as soon as the Medical Staff and the Management Committee had agreed on a new set of rules. Such a change was considered feasible since the more tightly organized Medical Staff could assume all the medical responsibilities and the management of the House Surgeons. They would also advise on the cleanliness and general condition of the Hospital.

Miss Hunter, under the direction of the Management Committee, would do all the office work, serve as admitting officer and take care of all except major purchases. With the administrative duties thus divided, the Board could make an interim appointment. Miss Flaws, Superintendent of Nurses, became Acting Superintendent and was bonded to take the post of Treasurer. Until her resignation a year later she was in charge of the non-medical staff and the day-to-day operation of the Hospital. Miss Elizabeth Campbell Gordon, who succeeded her, was appointed Lady Superintendent of the Kingston General Hospital, to start work 1 December 1904.

Among the many management problems over the next two years housekeeping was probably the most persistent and the most disturbing to the Management Committee. They felt that their Lady Superintendent should be able to cope with that problem better than the men could. The Board, remembering the assistance of the Ladies Committee of some ten years before in providing linen and raising money for other supplies, decided it should be revived. But they remembered also some problems with that committee. So they wrote to other hospitals to learn what duties had been given to their Ladies Aids and what assistance the ladies had given.

Miss Gordon was aghast at the meagre stock of linen and other supplies. Her comments may have influenced the Governors to decide immediately to invite the ladies of the community to form an auxiliary to assist the Hospital. On 15 February 1905, the Women's Aid Society of the Kingston General Hospital was formed with Mrs. J. C. Connell as its first president. By November they had 110 members and made a formal report to the annual meeting of the Board of Governors. They had restocked the Hospital with linen, bought cutlery and china, made doctors' aprons and nurses' gowns, collected bottles of fruit, and paid to have the Sampson Ward cleaned and painted.

There is some uncertainty regarding their sphere of activities during that first year. Their historian says that they inspected the Hospital and set up a visiting committee after their first meeting; but their President's Report indicates only supply work that first year and the 'otherwise' she mentions is not elaborated. The minutes of the Management Committee of the Board show that in April 1906 the Governors discussed asking the Women's Aid to visit the Hospital and that in June the Women's Aid appointed a visiting committee and agreed to meet with Management once a month to report on their visits. They made some shocking reports about the housekeeping which served to strengthen the opinion of the Board and the Medical Staff that a change in superintendents was overdue.

Miss Gordon caused one controversy, which was not limited to the Hospital, when she changed the uniform of the nurses in training from the traditional red and white to blue chambray with a modern bib, cap, and apron. The Alumnae, the Women's Aid, and the Medical Staff all objected and the argument went on for almost a year. The Board of Governors, under great pressure late in 1906, ruled that the thirty-five nurses then in Training School and all future students should again wear the red and white uniform, 'modernized'.

The Medical Staff had some trouble with Miss Gordon from the start. Within a few months of her taking charge, they asked for a number of changes in regulations and for clarification of areas of responsibility. They put Dr. Third and Dr. William Campbell in charge of the X-ray machine and directed them to hold the key to the machine. In November 1905 the staff passed a resolution that 'In the opinion of the Medical Staff many of the details of management of the Hospital are unsatisfactory and subversive to its best interests.' There were disagreements about treatment and about nursing care. Consequently there was general relief when the Board of Governors in September 1906 decided that the system of government by a Lady Superintendent must be ended if the best interests of the Hospital were to be preserved.

The Board reinstated the division of administrative duties with a man in command. Dr. A. D. MacIntyre was appointed Medical Superintendent; Miss Lizzie Tyson was appointed Superintendent of Nurses and Miss Stewart was appointed Matron to be in charge of housekeeping. The Women's Aid hired a laundress so that they could have control of the way the linen they had provided was cared for; and a year later they offered to pay for remodelling the laundry.

After the death of Dr. John Herald in 1905, Dr. Kilborn succeeded him as Chairman of the Medical Staff. During its executive sessions in 1906, the Staff was very busy rearranging the duties and terms of the House Surgeons so as to provide both a chain of authority and the continuity which had been lacking. The year was divided into three periods, with a retirement and a new appointment in each period so that there would always be available two House Surgeons with some experience.

The first House Surgeons appointed under this arrangement were Dr. Brown, Dr. Palmer, and Dr. Frederick Cays. To improve the clinical teaching, the Staff set up a committee to investigate the methods used and to provide for keeping case records at the Hospital. All the doctors were asked to cooperate in this project. Admission, birth, and death records were the only ones kept at the Hospital until that time; individual case records, even for the public ward patients, were the personal property of the attending physician.

The Medical Staff also considered the advisability of continuing a project started in 1903. At that time Dr. James Third had persuaded the Management Committee to erect a shack near the Hospital to try, on a small scale, the outdoor treatment of tuberculosis. Miss Alice Chown, Dr. Third, and a few others donated the $183 it cost to build the shack. Later, Captain Bruce Carruthers gave money to partition it and to add two windows. The next year the Medical Staff corresponded with the Muskoka Cottage Sanatorium to find out about their treatment of tuberculosis. Meanwhile, the doctors decided that cases in the initial stages could be put into the shack but that serious and terminal cases should be kept in the Hospital until a better place could be found. The problem was where in the Hospital to keep more tubercular patients. In the spring of 1906, the isolation wards at Hotel Dieu were closed and Kingston General Hospital had to accept all the cases of infectious diseases. Attics in Watkins and Main were renovated to take the advanced cases of TB; but the doctors agreed that the incurables needed a separate and proper building. The I.O.D.E. refurbished the Shack and continued to maintain it – until the cottage hospital plan was proposed in 1909. This plan resulted in the establishment of the Sir Oliver Mowat Memorial Hospital for Tuberculosis, on Portsmouth Avenue, just west of the city.

The Board of Governors' annual report for 1906 noted the deaths of Dr. Walkem, George Richardson, and John Mudie, and spoke of a closer cooperation with the Medical Staff and increased income from the City of Kingston and from pay patients. The appointment of a Medical Superintendent in 1906, however, was not the solution to all management problems as the Board had hoped it might possibly be. Nursing vied with housekeeping as the major problem. Superintendent of Nurses, Miss Tyson, resigned in January 1907; Miss Alice Scott stayed only two months, Miss Pickles about the same. Miss Bertha Willoughby was appointed in January 1909 to serve just over three years. The frequent changes were disruptive and the long periods between resignations and new appointments often left control of the nursing care and the nurses' training in the hands of recent graduates with little experience or authority.

In spite of this, the Training School prospered; for instance, in September 1908 there were ninety-nine applications for the six openings in the School. Student nurse Annie Baillie, then entering her third year, was proof of the value of careful selection of girls for the School, although the Governors who selected her could not have foreseen her long and devoted service to the Kingston General Hospital. The three-year training plan was working well according to the Management Committee reports to the Board.

The nurses themselves were not so sure. In August 1908 twenty-six nurses in training signed a formal complaint. They said the work was too hard; they were never sure of hours or days off; they often had to work overtime (day duty was 7 a.m. to 7 p.m. with no break); and they objected to having their mail censored. When the hours of duty were considered, along with the ratio of nurses per patient and the lack of conveniences, their complaints were not surprising. All of the nursing in this 184-bed Hospital was done by thirty-five nurses in training. The Superintendent of Nurses and the Night Supervisor were the only graduate nurses employed until 1908, when the Medical Staff asked that a graduate nurse be appointed Head Operating Room Nurse. She was directed to check the operating room instruments once a week and to report any missing or damaged instruments to the Medical Superintendent.

The nurses' work and responsibilities were complicated by the many changes in Matrons who had charge of the housekeeping and in cooks and kitchen help. Some left without notice because they objected to the unscheduled and careful inspections of the kitchens and other areas by members of the Women's Aid; others were dismissed. At times there was no one specifically in charge and Miss Hunter would then take on another job until a new matron or chief cook had been appointed. The Women's Aid, feeling that better wages would attract and keep more competent help, offered in 1908 to pay $25 a month for a housekeeper and linen woman.

The Women's Aid Society could afford to make such an offer for, as a fund-raising group, they had been most successful from the start. The more than $1,500 they raised in their second year enabled them not only to provide linen and other housekeeping supplies but also to make substantial payments toward maintenance and repair work on the Hospital buildings. Many of the citizens also continued to make private donations to the Hospital. The Misses Robertson, who followed a family tradition of giving to Kingston General Hospital, made such single gifts as twenty-eight pairs of woolen blankets and one hundred yards of sheeting. There was support also from some devoted Hospital staff: Joseph Scott, elevator operator, made a bequest of $561.64; Willie Glenn, who had been a servant and door man for over forty-three years, left $200 to the Hospital. The Women's Aid, however, a highly organized group of influential women, raised the greatest part of the donations to the Hospital as many who had formerly given directly to the Hospital now channelled their gifts through the Women's Aid. In 1907, they joined forces with the Board of Governors to organize a 'Made in Canada Fair' which raised over

$10,000 and that sum was increased by over $1,000 more through the personal efforts of Mrs. Neil Polson.

Such a large sum of money, for those days, solved some immediate and pressing problems for the Hospital. Although their income in 1906 had been $21,930.34, the largest in the history of the Hospital, they had an overdraft at the bank. The yearly income from paying patients had increased to $14,047.75 in 1907. But about three-quarters of the work of the Hospital was on behalf of public ward patients and outpatients. The Board consulted its lawyers to find if the Hospital could ask three dollars a week for charity and orphan patients from the City or the Orphans' Home, and still be eligible for the provincial grant as a charity hospital. (By 1911 the government was allowing the Hospital to charge seventy cents a day for poor admitted from the municipality.) Bookkeeping, however, for both the Hospital and the City was simplified if the money came as a yearly supporting grant. The county grant rose from $700 to $1,000, and the City grant was increased to $4,000, half of it assigned specifically to the contagious department. The Ontario government grant, however, had remained the same since 1895.

Expenses rose sharply; maintenance and repairs cost more. The Main Building needed a new roof and fire regulations had to be met with fire escapes, alarms and new fire extinguishers. More help was employed and salaries had to be increased. Emma Hunter was to get a salary of $500 a year from the first of October 1909, and the new Head Operating Room Nurse was paid $300 a year. Food costs had almost doubled, in spite of generous gifts of vegetables, meat, and bottled fruit, because the diet of all patients had improved under the scrutiny of the Women's Aid.

Their recommendations, however, did not always meet with approval. They once offered to replace a cracked laundry tub with a new wooden one. The Board recommended the purchase of a brass tub instead, and the ladies withdrew their offer. Although their historian says that their offer was later grudgingly accepted, the Management Committee minutes record the purchase of a brass tub. Another time the ladies made a recommendation to the Medical Staff about the beds assigned to tubercular patients and were told, politely but firmly, that such a matter was 'outside their jurisdiction'.

The new Medical Superintendent, Dr. H. A. Boyce, who had replaced Dr. MacIntyre in August 1908 was in sympathy with the doctors' desires for improvements in the facilities at the Hospital. The Medical Staff requested a microscope (purchased second-hand for $30), more thermometers and hypo-syringes, a · new sterilizer and an up-to-date X-ray machine. The requests were reasonable – those things were needed – but Hospital funds were limited so appeals were made to organizations and to individuals for specific gifts. The Women's Aid paid for the renovation of the Louise Operating Room, a job that put the L.O.R. out of use for some time because the W.A. found fault with the painter's work and made him repair it. The Napanee Women's Aid gave $400 for a glass cabinet and a supply of surgical instruments to be kept at the Hospital. (Most doctors still used their own.) The doctors themselves donated pieces of equipment; Dr. Campbell gave a wheeled carriage for the Doran operating room. The next December a Scheidel Western X-ray machine, costing $850, was purchased from Hospital funds.

Queen's Medical Faculty, aware that recent graduates were having trouble keeping up with the pace of medical discoveries, advertised in 1908 a three weeks summer course in Clinical Microscopy and Diagnosis, to be given by Dr. W. T. Connell. As Dr. James Third had written in the *Queen's Medical Quarterly* a year before, 'During the past fifteen years, the science of medicine has been progressing with extraordinary rapidity. Suspicions and half-truths of even a decade ago, are now arranged on the side of facts. The progress has been most marked, perhaps, in our knowledge of the causation of disease, and especially of the acute infectious disease. This has led to a better system of therapeutics and the advance has thus been general.' He closed the short article by saying, 'We recognize the fact that ninety-six per cent of the graduates settle down as general practitioners and we endeavour to fit them for their life work. . . .'

The Medical Staff of the Hospital, after not holding a formal meeting for almost two years, met in September 1910, to express their sympathy on the death of Dr. Isaac Wood. They decided that Dr. G. W. Mylks would take his place in Obstetrics and Gynaecology, as assistant to Dr. Garrett, and that Dr. A. R. B. Williamson would succeed Dr. Mylks in the surgical wards. They also expressed some dissatisfaction with the operation of the Hospital. They, therefore, recommended the reorganization of the work of the nurses and of the house staff, and the appointment of a satisfactory housekeeper. Evidently the housekeeping had not improved sufficiently to satisfy the doctors. The patients' meals were causing complaints and the Women's Aid offered to pay the wages of a qualified dietitian. Because it was difficult to find and keep a good one, a succession of dietitians began in July 1911.

Members of the Medical Staff were feeling very sensitive about some deficiencies at the Hospital, following the publication of the Flexner Report of 1910, a survey of the state of medical education in the United States and Canada. The report said, 'McGill and Toronto are excellent. Winnipeg and Kingston represent distinct effort toward higher levels.' The survey team, after spending part of one afternoon in Kingston and making, what the doctors said, was a very superficial inspection, commented: 'clinical facilities limited, obstetric cases too few, opportunity for out-patient work slight'. Yet the Queen's Medical Faculty was listed by the survey as a Class A school. The doctors were determined to keep it that way.

Private rooms at the Hospital were nearly always full and the doctors had for some time been making pleas for increased accommodation. The five hundred and eight Queen's student tickets were sold for the 1908–1909 session and a similar arrangement with the employees of the Locomotive Works severely taxed accommodation. The Board, keenly aware of the paying patients' contribution to the Hospital income, planned a new wing of private rooms and campaigned for funds. Sixty-five special donors gave $10,000; the City of Kingston gave $5,000. The Women's Aid gave $12,000, raised in one spectacular effort called 'A Festival of Empire' which was magnificently supported by local merchants.

In July 1912, the building was started; the Empire Wing was to cost $42,000. Scarcity of workmen and materials, plus the necessary suspension of work in the winter months, delayed the opening of the Empire Wing to April 1914; $10,000 was then still owing. The Wing had thirty bedrooms, twelve of them with grates and baths, nine bathrooms, three kitchens, and three wide halls. A seventy-five foot corridor provided the Wing with access to, but also isolation from, the Main Building. Queen's Medical Faculty members set up a Pathology Laboratory in the basement.

On the eve of World War I the Kingston General Hospital had over two hundred beds and in one year was treating over 2,100 patients in Hospital and about 1,500 outpatients. (Kingston's population was just over 21,000.) The death rate was 3.8 per cent, and the average stay was 14.6 days. Expenses had reached $46,500 a year, with income lagging a few hundred dollars behind, for although the government was giving greater assistance for indigent patients, costs had risen even more.

The Empire Wing provided the badly needed private rooms but the wards in the older buildings were over-crowded and extensive repairs were needed in flooring and plumbing. The heating system, if it could be glorified by calling it a system, with so many separate furnaces, was uneconomical in fuel and manpower. The Management Committee, therefore, recommended consideration of a central heating plant. Electricity was gradually replacing gas in the Hospital but it was not until after the war that there were electric lights in all the wards.

The new wing and greater capacity of the Hospital emphasized the inadequacies not only of the older buildings but also of much of the equipment. Increased emphasis on the prevention of disease put new sterilizers on the wanted list: one for mattresses, one for water and milk, one for the laundry. The new 'American Sterilizer' in the operating room had recently cost $875 and the doctors were asking for a new X-ray machine to replace the one bought five years before. The value of X-ray therapy had been discussed in 1913 in the first widely published article on cancer in newspapers and in the *Ladies Home Journal*. In April of 1914 the Hospital ordered a Wapperles X-ray machine to cost $1,200, and in November they bought a pulmotor to be installed in the operating room.

The British declaration of war against Germany on 4 August 1914 had little immediate effect on the Kingston General Hospital. Although five nurses left the 4th of October with the first Canadian contingent for overseas, things went on much as usual for a few months. Dr. Frederick Etherington, who had been a House Surgeon in 1902–1903, and then Professor of Anatomy at Queen's, was appointed to the surgical staff, and Dr. Williamson was moved to the gynaecological staff to harmonize with teaching assignments at Queen's. But the usual routine did not go on for long at Queen's or in the Hospital.

In the City it was not long before enlistments began to cut into the labour force. War needs stimulated production and by November the cotton and hosiery mills were working overtime, and the tannery and locomotive works signed new contracts. An influx of the families of men in training in Kingston army camps caused a housing shortage. A call for 3,500 more soldiers to be mobilized in the eastern district brought a frantic search for temporary barracks, in case they were all to be trained in Kingston. Victoria School and the two big halls in the City Building were offered as possible barracks. It was also suggested that three steamers tied up side by side in the harbour could accommodate six hundred men.

Fort Henry was used as a prisoner of war camp. On 30 November 1914, the *Daily Standard* reported that seventy-five more prisoners had arrived to bring the total in the Fort to more than five hundred. Over a hundred prisoners were moved to Petawawa a few months later to help relieve the crowding. A mutiny of the prisoners early in 1915 brought an angry reaction from Kingstonians shocked by the recent heavy losses of Canadians at the Battle of Ypres. One man, writing to the paper, volunteered to get up a firing squad to quell any further trouble. War fever had taken over.

Many Queen's students and faculty enlisted. Those left on campus organized an officers' training corps, making sure that it would count as one subject on the year's work. On 4 December 1914, Queen's Medical Faculty met to organize a Hospital Corps for service overseas. They planned to have eight officers, sixty-five men and eighteen nurses. When their plans were approved early in 1915 by the Militia Department, they appealed for donations to equip the Corps, and received prompt and generous response from friends and townspeople. While the Corps was gathering equipment other volunteers did not wait. About thirty members of the final year in Medicine were granted degrees and left the middle of February to join the staff of the Duchess of Connaught's Hospital at Cliveden. The Queen's Stationary Hospital No. 5 left on 5 May 1915, expecting the war to be over in a few months. Dr. Etherington was the Lt.-Colonel commanding the Corps, with surgeons Capt. C. E. Kidd, Lt. Ballantyne, Lt. Polson; civil surgeons Doctors Anglin, W. T. Connell and Garfield Platt; dental surgeon, Capt. Ernest Sparks; radiographer,

Lt. J. P. Quigley and Quartermaster, Capt. James Wallace. Dr. W. T. Connell
was ordered back to Kingston at the end of the year to help speed up the training
and graduation of medical officers. He was also in command of the Grant Hall
Hospital and he continued to be in command after it was moved to St. Helen's and
was called the Sydenham Hospital.

Patriotic concerts, collections for the Belgian Relief Fund, and donations to the
Red Cross tended to overshadow local charity needs. By Christmas the Hospital felt
the impact of a war economy and was urgently in need of generous donations. No
merchant would offer tenders for supplies; the Hospital had to try for the best price
on the open market. A number of preparations used in medicine and surgery,
which had come mainly from Germany, were in very limited supply and prices
skyrocketed. Hospital finances were strained and so was accommodation, when
the military units training in the area sent in more measles and chickenpox cases
than the isolation wing could hold. The laundry had to have some quick and
necessary improvements to take the added work load; the old steam engine for the
washing machine broke down and was replaced by an electric motor.

Everyone worked overtime, for the biggest problem through all the war years
was the maintenance of an adequate staff in all departments. Even additional
student nurses were accepted more rapidly than suitable accommodation could be
found for them. The nursing staff had constant changes; Miss Lydia Elmsley was
replaced as Superintendent of Nurses by Miss Claudia Boskill; as student nurses
graduated they were immediately given extra responsibilities at the Hospital but
they left very soon for military service. Olevia Wilson graduated in May 1916, and
was made Head Operating Room Nurse. She resigned in October to serve at the
military hospital before she went overseas early in 1917. A permanent housekeeping
staff was an impossibility; maids, orderlies, and cooks came and went in all too short
a time in spite of raises in pay. Even the Women's Aid seems to have been busy
elsewhere.

The management problems of supplies and help were complicated by administrative changes. Dr. H. A. Boyce, Medical Superintendent for seven years, left in
May 1915. He was followed as Superintendent over the next year and a half by
three men: Dr. D. A. Coon, Dr. M. F. Coglin, and Dr. J. R. Boyd, each of whom
stayed less than six months. With the Hospital busier than it ever had been before,
the frequent changes of personnel, both in administration and in the services, threw
a heavy burden on those who stayed. Miss Claudia Boskill, Superintendent of
Nurses, and Miss Emma Hunter, Secretary, saw that the necessary work was
carried on to support the remaining staff doctors and to care for the patients. Miss
Hunter's duties, as noted early in 1917, were to purchase supplies, admit patients,
supervise the housekeeping and the general female help, keep the records and make

reports. The Management Committee recommended that she be given some office help – if it could be found. She was often seen on a Saturday at the farmers' market, accompanying Colonel Kent, the Chairman of the Board, and followed by Isaac Plunket, a porter, with a two-wheeled cart, as she bought chickens and vegetables. Some, no doubt, were for the interns' table over which she presided for many years.

The Kingston General Hospital in 1916 admitted 4,016 patients and accommodation was taxed to the utmost. There were other hospitals taking military patients; Queen's leased Grant Hall to the Military Hospital and Convalescent Homes Commission. St. Helen's (Sydenham Hospital) and the Mowat Tuberculosis Hospital were both used as military hospitals and they all needed non-medical, nursing, and medical personnel. The dearth of medical men was serious. Fewer students were entering medical training and the usual quota of graduates was not available to take up practice or hospital positions. More were needed overseas also, as the call went out for 154 men for the Queen's Stationary Hospital, then in Cairo. At the end of 1916 it seemed as if the war might go on forever.

The Medical Staff at the Kingston General Hospital, chaired by Dr. James Third after the death of Dr. R. K. Kilborn, met early in December 1916 to discuss the qualifications of a new Medical Superintendent. With the disruptions in Hospital management caused by constantly changing personnel, they felt that it was absolutely essential that the new Medical Superintendent should have had some administrative experience in a hospital. They said that the man recommended by the Board was qualified to do little more administrative work than that already capably handled by Emma Hunter, and thus refused to endorse his appointment. The Board, R. E. Kent chairman, accepted the doctors' recommendation that Dr. J. C. Wright, then an assistant to Dr. Edward Ryan at Rockwood Hospital, be appointed Medical Superintendent of the Hospital. Doctors Third, Williamson, J. C. Connell, and W. T. Connell comprised the committee to discuss management and policy with the new man, to settle priorities and to lay future plans. Nothing more than absolutely essential maintenance was immediately possible because of shortages of money, material, and manpower. But there would have to be considerable expansion as soon as the war was over and careful advance planning was necessary.

On 5 March 1917, Dean J. C. Connell announced that Dr. James Douglas, Chancellor of Queen's University, would 'give $100,000 toward a fund to develop the Kingston General Hospital into a capacious, modern institution and especially with a view to improvement of the teaching facilities and making research possible'. Queen's made this proposal as one of the partners in the charity Hospital. Within two days the University and the Hospital had set up a joint committee regarding the Hospital extension and were hard at work putting on paper needs they had been discussing for over a year. Dr. J. C. Connell was chairman with Doctors Williamson, Sparks, Boyce, and Third working with J. M. Farrell, A. F. Chown, N. C. Polson, Jr., J. A. Minnes, Francis King, and R. E. Kent.

The plans drafted by this Building Committee were the basis for what became known later as the Fifteen Year Plan. In their discussions they considered eight items, listed in what seemed to them the proper priority:

1. New building for wards to double the present capacity
2. Dispensary
3. Laundry
4. Central heating plant
5. Adequate quarters for nurses
6. Isolation hospital for 75 to 100 patients
7. Outdoor department
8. Accommodation for nervous cases

When the Rev. R. Bruce Taylor succeeded Daniel Gordon as Principal of Queen's University in December 1917, some of the committee's recommendations were ready for the architects. By 30 August 1918 their architects, Stevens and Lee of Boston and Toronto, presented an estimate for the complete plan totalling $626,000. The Building Committee had to decide on priorities in implementing the plan, and to start a campaign for more funds. Municipal and provincial governments were approached, and in May 1919 it was announced that the Ontario government had voted $400,000 to Queen's University for improvements in the Kingston General Hospital.

While examining the needs of the Hospital and preparing plans there was also searching examination of the relationship of the University and the Hospital. Queen's, until now a fairly silent partner in this charity, providing medical staff and receiving clinical teaching privileges, had assumed an important role as the wealthy partner, or, at least, the one through whom the money had come. The University was in an excellent bargaining position. Members of the Queen's Medical Faculty, being also the Medical Staff of the Hospital, asked for a firm agreement with the Board of Governors on control of all appointments to the Visiting Staff and also of appointments of interns. They wanted an agreement that non-staff doctors could attend patients only in private or semi-private rooms, guaranteeing the availability of all ward patients for clinical instruction of the medical students. This reversed the Board's decision of 1901, which allowed non-staff doctors to attend ward patients; but current opinion supported the recommendation of the Medical Staff that the wards must be freely open to clinical study. Such an arrangement was absolutely essential in order to counter the proposal that all clinical departments of the Queen's Medical Faculty should be moved to Ottawa where sufficient clinical material could be assured.

The Charity Hospital for the treatment of the sick and injured had to recognize that its educational and scientific functions were increasing in importance. Should a medical school have its own hospital or should a hospital develop its own medical school? In Kingston Queen's Medical Faculty and the Kingston General Hospital might have to exist separately but their very existence depended on their working closely and harmoniously together. The Board of Governors signed the agreement as the war came to an end and the Hospital became crowded with 'flu patients.

Seven

Canadians at the close of the war, after the joyful celebrations mixed with sorrow *Fifteen Year* for the terrible losses, felt a relief from tension and a hope that life might soon *Building Plan* return to normal. They were war weary but optimistic that the economy which had *and the* developed to meet war needss, might now be diverted to help a quick return to the *Depression* good old days. But rapid adjustment to peacetime was not going to be possible. The *1919–1939* good old days, before the conscription controversy and new political alignments, were gone forever with the new development of urban industrialism and a more complex way of life.

The general economy had to be considered as still on a war footing. With about 300,000 soldiers being demobilized, the government recognized that pensions for those veterans would cost millions. The returned soldiers would also immediately swell the work force and, in an attempt to cope with this problem, sixty employment offices were set up across the country to find work for veterans as well as for those who would lose war production jobs. It was soon evident that generous land settlement opportunities were not so attractive to the veterans as the possibility of urban employment. But industry could not absorb the sudden influx of mainly unskilled workers. Consequently, the trade union movement, growing under wartime demands for labourers, gained new impetus in the post-war boom of the early twenties. Manufactured goods were needed both here and abroad; but, as stocks were low and individual wartime savings available, prices on scarce goods rose to new heights.

Changes in the economy were accompanied by changes in social conditions and in moral standards. Urban centres grew in population and in problems. Women had achieved with the vote, new freedom and influence. There was a reaction against the Victorian prudery which had concealed such problems as the high incidence of venereal disease discovered in the medical examination of army recruits. The medical profession persuaded the government in 1919 to establish the Federal Department of Health. And the Dominion Council of Health acted to coordinate federal and provincial health agencies, introducing grants-in-aid to set up centres for the treatment of venereal disease.

The governments, federal, provincial, and municipal, needed also to coordinate their efforts in providing assistance for the old, the disabled, and the needy who could no longer be supported solely by private charity. Widows and orphans of servicemen, and returned veterans were the biggest immediate problem because, although the federal government had set up a Soldiers' Civil Reestablishment Programme, administrative delays and misunderstandings left many in desperate circumstances. The Salvation Army, in January 1919, called for contributions to its national Million Dollar Fund to assist the returning men and their families.

Kingston people went almost daily out to the Grand Trunk Station to meet the troop trains bringing men to be demobilized in this area. Some veterans were taken directly to Grant Hall Hospital or to the Sydenham Military Hospital to join the sick and disabled already there. Others who wanted to stay in Kingston looked for places to live. But the housing shortage, caused by the rapid growth of the population and limited domestic building in the war years, was a poor welcome for the veterans. The City Council at its first meeting in 1919 set up a committee to study the local situation and to find out what other governments were prepared to do.

Council also considered improving the harbour to ensure that Kingston would continue to be a transshipment point for the bigger lake ships which could now use the enlarged Welland Canal. Over a hundred vessels wintered in Kingston and were good for city business when they were equipped in the spring. It was important to keep that business.

Kingston felt the impact also of general social change. An international organizer of textile workers came to the city to investigate the cotton mill strike. Other visitors were members of the National Council of Women meeting in executive session. They paid tribute to the achievement of Mrs. Alexander Newlands, the first woman elected to the Kingston Board of Education. Women were active as always in organized welfare work: the Victorian Order of Nurses reported that it had made 2,140 visits in 1918, and had established a Child Welfare Station on Barrie Street.

Of course, whether in war or peace, many things went on as usual. The theatres were always busy; the sports were read first by many, for as the editor had said in the war years, hockey scores to some readers were more important even than the war news. The change to peacetime activities was perhaps most striking when the

Kingston Armouries housed the spring Poultry Show. But there was still plenty to remind people of the past four years.

The sad aftermath of war, the great number of sick, wounded, and disabled veterans, extended many of the wartime problems of the hospitals well into the post-war period. Temporary military hospitals and new veterans' hospitals relieved some of the pressure on accommodation. But they also increased the problem of a sufficient number of trained personnel, both medical and non-medical, to staff the hospitals.

Early in December 1918, the Medical Staff of the Kingston General Hospital met to plan the reorganization which would be necessary when staff members would return from war service. They also made recommendations to the Management Committee on the needs of the Hospital. Most urgently needed was a superintendent, since Dr. Wright had resigned in September and Dr. D. C. Matheson had agreed to accept only a temporary appointment. He was a young anatomist who, on the recommendation of Dean J. C. Connell, had been getting some practical experience at the Hospital as a Clinical Fellow. Dr. Matheson said that his main function as Superintendent seemed to be to administer anaesthetics almost every morning for operations on public ward patients. As he taught anatomy at Queen's in the afternoons, most of the Hospital administration was handled by the Chairman of Management, the Chairman of Medical Staff, and Miss Hunter, who managed, as usual, the day-to-day running of the Hospital.

Disruptions of the war years convinced the Medical Staff and the Board of Governors of the need for a better organization and for a full-time, qualified administrator. They needed a man who could win the cooperation of all concerned to make the best use of the planned facilities. There was, however, no general agreement on where to look for such a man, on what his qualifications should be or what direction the reorganization should take.

While discussions on those problems continued, the Medical Staff reached early agreement on the organization of their services and on how to achieve expansion of the Hospital Medical Staff and of the Queen's Medical Faculty. They set up seven services, to include indoor and outdoor patients. The head of each service at the Hospital was to be head of the corresponding department at the University. Those doctors would constitute the Medical Board or Staff Executive at the Hospital. At the end of the 1919 session at Queen's, Dr. W. T. Connell went to Britain to look for new staff for Medicine, Surgery, and Pathology. The result of his trip was the appointment, during the next year, of Doctors G. S. Melvin, L. J. Austin, and James Miller.

Retirements and shifts in the teaching staff at Queen's were accompanied, as agreed, by changes in the Medical Staff at the Hospital. Dr. D. E. Mundell continued to act as Chief of Surgery. But a second service in Surgery was set up in charge of Dr. L. J. Austin, formerly of The London Hospital. Dr. Austin, aged forty when he came to Kingston in 1920, had been trained at Cambridge and served at the London Hospital until he joined the British Red Cross at the beginning of the war. He was one of the first prisoners of war and after his release in 1915, served with the Royal Army Medical Corps, returning to The London in 1918. Dr. Lorimer John Austin was known affectionately to staff and students as 'Blimey'. He was, as Dr. W. A. Jones wrote, 'an able man, an excellent teacher with a great gift for imparting knowledge, and, for his day and generation, an accomplished surgeon'. As many Queen's medical students could tell, he kept himself poor helping others. He was also a most unconventional man, the delight of all who appreciated an eccentric character.

Dr. James Third, who had served the Hospital as Superintendent from 1896 to 1900 and then had been a member of the Attending Staff, retired. He was replaced as a member of both the Queen's and the Hospital staff by Dr. E. C. D. MacCallum. Dr. Walter T. Connell, having developed an intense interest in clinical medicine during his military hospital service, left the Department of Bacteriology and Pathology. He took over Dr. Third's post as Chief of Medicine at the Hospital and as Head of the Department of Medicine at Queen's University. His former duties were assumed by Dr. G. B. Reed in Bacteriology and Dr. James Miller in Pathology. Dr. G. Spencer Melvin, a physiologist, joined Dr. Connell's staff in Medicine.

Dr. J. P. Quigley, who had served as radiologist with the Queen's University Hospital unit in Cairo, was put in charge of the X-ray work at the Kingston General Hospital. Since he also held the same position at both the Hotel Dieu and the Sydenham Military Hospital, he could do little more than direct the work of other members of staff, who were less qualified or less experienced. The Medical Staff recommended the hiring of a physician to be in charge of X-ray, full-time at the Hospital and limited to that service. Dr. Quigley was offered the position but, as he was not prepared to limit himself to X-ray or to one hospital, the part-time arrangement continued. His recommendations regarding equipment, housing, and maintenance were accepted, and in 1920 a new X-ray machine was installed in the basement of the Empire Wing.

Also in 1920, the Kingston General Hospital was approved by the American College of Physicians and Surgeons. The staff at that time was as follows:

Medical Staff of the Kingston General Hospital

MEDICINE
Head of Service	Dr. W. T. Connell
Assistants	Dr. E. C. D. MacCallum
	Dr. William Gibson, Dr. J. P. Quigley
	Dr. H. A. Boyce, Dr. G. S. Melvin

SURGERY
Head of Service A	Dr. D. E. Mundell
Head of Service B	Dr. L. J. Austin
Assistants	Dr. J. F. Sparks, Dr. S. J. Keyes
	Dr. R. J. Gardiner, Dr. I. G. Bogart

OBSTETRICS
Head of Service	Dr. A. R. B. Williamson
Assistant	Dr. J. F. Sparks

GYNAECOLOGY
Head of Service	Dr. G. W. Mylks
Assistant	Dr. J. F. Sparks
Assistant in Paediatrics	Dr. H. E. Day

EYE, EAR, NOSE AND THROAT
Head of Service	Dr. J. C. Connell
Assistant	Dr. F. A. Cays

ANAESTHETICS
Head of Service	Dr. S. J. Keyes

PATHOLOGY
Head of Service	Dr. James Miller
Assistant	Dr. Thomas Little
Physiological Chemist	Dr. D. Lothrop
Clinical Assistant	Dr. G. B. Reed

The major expansion of the Hospital, as envisaged by the Building Committee in its 1917 report, was the subject of continuing discussions. After the architects gave their estimate of the cost of the whole plan, the committee re-examined the priorities and decided to place the heating plant, the service building, and a new public ward building at the top of the list. The May 1919 provincial government grant of $400,000 added to the promised gift of $100,000 from Chancellor Douglas, made the architects' figure of $626,000 seem compassable. Yet further examination of costs, materials, and priorities caused the Building Committee to decide, in February 1921, not to proceed with any great amount of work because of the high cost of building.

The Service Building, to house kitchens, staff dining rooms, and some staff bedrooms, was, however, an absolute and immediate necessity. When the tenders were opened on 11 June 1921, the Dickie Construction Company received the contract.

At the same time, the Building Committee, which had been working hard for five years, was reconstituted. Dean J. C. Connell remained as chairman. Board members R. E. Kent, Principal Bruce Taylor, W. F. Nickle, Elmer Davis, J. M. Campbell, James Richardson, and Dr. A. E. Ross made up the new committee. The construction of a joint heating plant to serve both Queen's and the Hospital was most thoroughly investigated by both partners and was given top priority. The original estimate for the building, chimney, equipment, and tunnels was $250,000. Contracts were awarded in May 1922, and the whole complex, power house and engineering laboratories, was in operation in 1923.

Meanwhile the Building Committee considered plans for an extension to the Empire Wing to provide twenty-four more private rooms. They considered the cost ($67,000) unreasonable but they authorized the building of the extension because those private rooms would be a source of much needed income. The proposed separate isolation hospital, which had been sixth on the original list, became a matter of negotiation with the City Council. The provision for care of those with contagious diseases was, by law, the responsibility of the municipality. On 1 March 1920, the City Council passed a by-law to erect and equip an Isolation Hospital at a cost of not more than $150,000. When the cost rose they authorized an additional $25,000 and asked Mayor Hugh Nickle to sit with the Building Committee for further decisions on the Isolation Hospital. The City built the hospital on a site provided by the Kingston General Hospital, on King Street opposite the new heating plant.

The Board of Governors at this time bought other land on both sides of King Street, including the knitting mill, the box factory, and other properties for the future expansion of the General Hospital. Building plans and operations took the major attention of the Board and a good deal of the time of the Medical Staff, who wanted some control of the kind of facilities they would work with. Construction also caused problems in the regular operation of the Hospital; the noise and confusion were hard on staff and patients. In the older buildings only minimum maintenance was done; they would be renovated later, but meanwhile they had to be used to more than capacity. The washrooms for staff and patients were unsightly and unsanitary; and the old and deteriorating plumbing caused damage to walls and floors in Watkins and Main. Surgeons complained about the state of the operating rooms and asked that the old wash basins be replaced by modern ones with elbow taps and foot wastes.

The biggest problem, however, was personnel. Dr. Matheson had submitted his resignation in March 1920, and was still awaiting his replacement in September. Brigadier General (Dr.) A. E. Ross, M.P., agreed to act in a temporary capacity until the next session of Parliament in February 1921. When that time came, the Board persuaded him to continue as Superintendent and gave him an assistant so that he could be free to attend Parliament. It was another interim, partly political appointment, not popular with the Medical Staff because it delayed again the appointment of a proper, full-time administrator. This part-time, off-and-on arrangement continued for two and a half years.

The nursing staff had problems too. In November 1920, Miss Claudia Boskill resigned. She had been Superintendent of Nurses for eight years, six of them the difficult war and immediate post-war years. The nursing staff had grown from 38 student nurses in 1912, to three graduate supervisors and 88 student nurses in 1920. There were fewer applicants for the Training School, however, and Miss Boskill recommended that an honorarium be once again offered to student nurses. Other changes were needed too. The Nurses' Home had been very satisfactory in 1903, but was now seriously overcrowded. It had only six wash bowls, two bath-tubs, and two toilets for 36 nurses. The George Street home, bought in 1919 to house nurses who were then in a private rooming house, was crowded; so was the nurses' floor in the Nickle Wing. More room had to be found immediately. When the new Service Building was finished in April 1923, 22 nurses moved into the top floor. That space had been designed to house the maids and the kitchen help who had to remain in basement rooms in the old buildings.

Miss Patience Carey, appointed Superintendent of Nurses in December 1920, had almost immediately to cope with a problem in discipline. The records do not show why, but three student nurses were suspended for six months. They were warned that 'any misbehaviour regarding the Hospital or interference with the nursing school or circulating of slanderous reports will be considered against them when appearing before Management at the end of the suspension'. A very few days later Management held a special meeting to consider a threat that the whole nursing staff would go on strike unless the three nurses were reinstated. The Medical Staff asked the Board to reconsider the suspension. By the end of January two of the suspended nurses were back in training and the third, having completed her three years, had been granted her diploma and left. But problems continued over the next two years until the Nurses' Training School had a new set of rules.

Miss Boskill, in her final 1920 report, paid tribute to Miss Emma Hunter for her work and support during the five years of so many changes in medical super-intendents, house surgeons and supervisors. She might also have mentioned the even more frequent changes in matrons, dietitians, cooks, and maids. In spite of some small increases, the meagre pay for hospital jobs was not sufficient to attract or to hold a good permanent staff. The Women's Aid offered to pay for an increase in the dietitian's salary. That was a more welcome communication to the badly harassed Management Committee than one which noted that the visiting ladies had found two taps running, and eight cups with no handles in the nurses' dining room.

The Women's Aid took a very definite and helpful step in May 1921, when, being again dismayed by the sad state of the housekeeping, they hired four char-women to clean up the Hospital. The ladies took turns supervising the work for a few weeks, but when they found it was a much bigger job than they anticipated, they asked Emma Hunter to take over the supervision. Meantime they replaced the badly depleted stock of linen and suggested that if the laundry methods were improved the linen would last longer. It is not clear why the order was given, but in June 1922, Miss Carey, Superintendent of Nurses, was directed in the future to accompany the Women's Aid visiting ladies on their tours of the Hospital.

Wages were a matter of concern also for the Medical Staff. They reported in 1921 that it was impossible to get graduate interns without pay and they recommended that interns be offered fifty dollars a month, Queen's to pay half of it. The doctors also asked that a permanent clerk be appointed whose first duty would be to keep patient records. The Board agreed but it took some time to find the proper person and longer to organize what records there were. Record clerks, working under pressure, without much system, did not stay long. Consequently patient histories and medical reports were often incomplete and usually late. In 1923, a new system of records was introduced, to meet the standards of the American College of Surgeons defined in 1918. The value of the records depended on the close cooperation of the doctors and many of them, especially the older ones, were very lax in completing records on their patients. In September 1923 the Medical Staff asked the Board to *require* all physicians or surgeons practising in the Hospital to write patients' histories and progress notes themselves or arrange to have interns do it.

As diagnostic services increased, there were many more items to note on these patient records. The new cardiograph, installed in January 1921, replaced a huge, old Cambridge string galvonometer. The Medical Staff set up a scheme for systemic examinations. There was also more X-ray work as the doctors increased their use of the improved equipment. They called for new chemical and biological tests to support their diagnosis and the laboratories had to be expanded. As it was no longer economic or safe to have medicines compounded by any or every doctor or intern, the Medical Staff hired a trained pharmacist to take charge of the dispensary in 1925. There also were extra services for patients; Dr. H. E. Day had an outdoor clinic for children open every Thursday, and a Genito-Urinary clinic was started.

The increase in Hospital services did not bring a corrresponding increase in numbers of patients. In 1922 the Board complained that a healthy season was hard on Hospital finances. Actually there were a few more patients that year than there had been even during the influenza epidemic, in the very busy 1918–1919 season. The number of operations continued to increase; in 1923 there were 2,335 compared to 736 operations performed in 1912. That was a more expensive kind of treatment and rates had not been increased enough to cover it, especially for the public ward patients. The income from pay patients continued to be one of the main sources of income. Compare the figures for 1913 and 1923.

	Income	Expenses	Pay patients	Pay Roll	Patients admitted
1913	$ 41,963	$ 41,457	$24,649	$ 8,843	2,108
1923	136,089	140,790	95,013	34,980	3,712

Government grants also increased. The provincial government paid fifty cents per patient per day in 1923, compared to less than thirty cents in 1917. The municipal government obligation for indigent patients was set by the 1912 Hospital and Charitable Institutions Act at a per diem rate of $1. By 1923 the limit had been raised to $1.25. In Kingston the City Council continued to make a lump sum payment ($12,000 in 1922), preferring that to the more complicated bookkeeping and necessary proofs in the per diem rate. Unfortunately for the Hospital, the flat sum from Kingston meant a sizeable loss on indigent patients from the City.

Private donations to the general operating fund were neither so large nor so regular as they had been before the war. There were still, however, a number of contributors who made a tradition of regular and generous gifts to the Hospital. Benjamin W. Robertson, who died in 1921, was one of the oldest Life Governors and, with other members of his family, a long time benefactor of the Hospital. The Board of Governors, in 1922, paid tribute to him and to other Governors and benefactors such as Byron M. Britton and John Bell Carruthers. There were legacies from such men as William Fee, Prof. Nathan F. Dupuis, Richard Waldron, and R. G. Richardson. The Kiwanis Club gave $400 to help improve the hot water system. Many gave money for special memorial rooms – McIver, Scobell-Kinghorn, Dalton, and others. A modest amount came almost every year from the Women's Aid, although their biggest contribution was still in supplying linen for the Hospital.

The Board had occasion soon to acknowledge generous gifts from two other benefactors. Frederick Welch, who had chaired the campaign for the Sir Oliver Mowat Memorial Hospital, left a bequest of almost $16,000 to be used for the benefit and comfort of indigent patients in the Kingston General Hospital. In June 1923, Charles S. Campbell, eldest son of Sir Alexander Campbell of Kingston, died in Montreal. He left one fifth of his considerable estate to the Kingston General Hospital. It was the largest single gift to the Hospital, amounting in the end to well over $350,000. The estate was finally settled after the death, from old age, of Mr. Campbell's favourite horse 'Kodak', who had been provided for under the will.

Kingston General Hospital's campaign for funds to finance new buildings continued during this whole period. Individual donations added to government grants and although construction costs were rising, the expansion of the Hospital continued. In November 1922, Mrs. Alice Richardson, widow of Senator Henry W.

Richardson (1855–1918), offered to give $100,000 to provide a building which would include suitable accommodation for tuberculosis patients. (The Mowat Hospital, built for the treatment of tuberculosis, had been in use as a veterans' hospital.) This Richardson gift made possible an early start on the buildings opened in 1925 as the Richardson Laboratories and the Douglas Wing.

One new building required some special decisions by the Management Committee. The Isolation Hospital was built with City funds on Hospital grounds, to house patients who were, by law, the responsibility of the municipality. Late in 1923, when it was almost finished, there was still no formal arrangement for its administration, operation, and supervision. The Board of Governors of the Hospital agreed to manage the Isolation Hospital as a separate institution on a one-year trial; and made sure that the City's financial obligations were clearly understood. This arrangement continued as long as there was a separate Isolation Hospital. Miss Lillian Gill was appointed Supervising Nurse of Isolation at $85 a month and Mr. and Mrs. Nicholson as caretaker and cook at a combined salary of $75 a month.

Other personnel and management problems plagued the Board. In May 1923, Dr. A. E. Ross resigned and Dr. J. H. Pilkey, who had been his assistant over the past two years, became Acting Superintendent. The decision regarding a new superintendent was critical and a committee on Hospital management and administration was set up to find a man. They reported at a special meeting in August, recommending the appointment of Mr. F. Taylor, Superintendent of St. Luke's Hospital in Ottawa. The Board disagreed at first and it was not until November that Mr. Taylor became the first male, lay Superintendent of the Kingston General Hospital. (The previous two had been women who were also Superintendents of Nurses.) Dr. W. T. Connell, Chairman, and Dr. W. A. Jones, Secretary of the Medical Staff, met with Mr. Taylor to discuss a number of changes in the control of medical matters which had to be made under this new arrangement.

Other changes were needed too. Assistants to Miss Carey left, one after another; housekeepers and dietitians stayed only a few months; student nurses were unhappy. In February 1924, Miss Patience Carey resigned as Superintendent of Nurses to leave March 31st. Doctors W. T. Connell, L. J. Austin, and G. W. Mylks met with Col. R. E. Kent and his Management Committee to interview applicants for the post. Two women were offered the position and refused it. Then, in June, Miss Annie Baillie, who had entered the Nurses Training School as a probationer in October 1907, was offered the job. She accepted as of August first. Miss Baillie had served with the Queen's Hospital Unit in Cairo during the war and nursed at Ongwanada (Sydenham Military Hospital) after the war. She then took a position at the Hanneman Hospital in Scranton, Pennsylvania. In July 1924 she returned to Kingston.

Miss Baillie faced an immediate problem of restoring the Nurses' Training School to the quality it once had, for it had suffered under some difficulties for a few years. It had been removed from the New York registered school list until it could be reorganized and inspected. The Chairman of the Board of Governors, the Chairman of the Medical Staff, Dr. W. T. Connell, and Dr. Frederick Etherington became the Advisory Committee of the Training School.

The new Superintendent of Nurses made a number of very definite recommendations when she accepted the job.

1. Appointment of a full-time instructress for the School.
2. Supervisors for Empire and Doran.
3. A supervisor for Watkins and the wards.
4. An assistant superintendent of nurses.
5. Special nurses to be under the Superintendent of Nurses with rules set by her.
6. If no graduate nurse available for special duty the Superintendent to put a student nurse on at a charge to the patient of $3 a day.
7. New rules to be submitted re late leaves, etc.
8. More orderlies.

Most of Miss Baillie's recommendations were approved by the Board who were relieved to have positive and constructive suggestions rather than complaints. Miss Louise D. Acton of Ottawa was appointed Instructress and Miss Olevia Wilson, Assistant Superintendent of Nurses in charge of Watkins and the public wards. A new standard of two years of high school or its equivalent was set for entrance to the Training School; a medical examination and vaccination were also made compulsory. And more accommodation was provided for nurses in the Nickle Wing on what had been the scarlet fever floor.

In September 1924, Superintendent Taylor, unable to cope with the situation, resigned as of December. Once again the discussion began; should there be a lay or a medical superintendent? This time the committee, all non-medical men, recommended that the Board seek the advice of an outside expert in Hospital management. Dr. J. C. Connell objected that 'the Hospital requires a man, whether lay or medical, not a report.' However, Dr. Horace L. Brittain of Toronto, head of a firm of hospital management consultants, was hired to make a report by the end of the year. The Board gave special thanks, at the annual meeting, to its retiring Chairman, Col. R. E. Kent, for devotion to the Hospital 'over years of war and want'. Mr. Hugh C. Nickle became Chairman to serve for three years. They were years of energetic reorganization at the Hospital and Mr. Nickle's belief in the future of the Hospital was of great assistance in long range plans.

On 29 December 1924, the Brittain Report was considered at a special meeting of the Board of Governors. Dr. Brittain was impressed with the potential quality of the Kingston General Hospital; the connection with Queen's University made it very attractive; the Medical Staff was very good, the nursing very good. Relatively speaking, the management was good but the business end was poor and needed both complete reorganization and the application of sound business methods. 'Having a competent Medical Staff, a well-organized Nursing and Interne Division, the chief problem is to operate from a financial and administrative basis so that funds are available to give the Medical and nursing divisions the facilities and supporting services they require.'

The Report went on to deal with recommendations for a superintendent for the Kingston General Hospital:

> In the opinion of the writer, based on detailed study of the duties of a superintendent, in teaching hospitals, the chief qualifications required in a superintendent are:
>
>   1. Administrative ability and experience.
>   2. Force of character.
>   3. Good general education.
>   4. Ability to co-operate and secure co-operation.
>   5. Ability to meet the public.
>   6. An instinct for economy.

The question has been raised whether or not the superintendent should be a medical man. The writer's opinion is that this is an entirely secondary consideration in the operation of any hospital, particularly of a teaching hospital. In an open hospital which has not the advantages of university connection to guarantee good medical and surgical control, it may become necessary, in some cases, to have a superintendent who is a medical man and who, on account of his prestige, can insist on proper standards; but, in a hospital which has full time or even half time heads of medical, surgical and other services, the conditions are quite different.

The line of progress is not necessarily toward a medical superintendent, but toward the increasing of the facilities, for supervision of the professional staff.

In a teaching hospital, a superintendent may be a medical man, but in reality he cannot be a medical superintendent. He is, and must be, specifically excluded from the treatment of the sick. His relations to the medical staff, except perhaps in grave emergency, are not professional but simply disciplinary and administrative, and in these days, the possibility of such emergency arising is extremely remote. If sufficient care is taken and importance allocated to the appointment of the senior member of the resident staff, all conceivable emergencies will be adequately taken care of.

... The main thing is to get an administrator of education, good sense and ability who stands on his rights but recognizes the limitations of his proper field. Ninety-five per cent of a superintendent's duties are purely administrative without any direct reference to medical or surgical control. His duty is not to treat the sick, but to bring about the conditions and render the services necessary for proper care of the sick by those whose function it is. It is his duty to supply, under the Board, the tools and workshops in good condition. In fine, the first requirement is a good superintendent. If he is also a medical man, but with his first interest being in administration and not in medicine, he has an additional but not essential qualification.

. . . Granted a limited amount of money for the superintendent's salary, it would seem that on the average the best value can be obtained from a lay superintendent.

Dr. Brittain recommended for the job Mr. R. Fraser Armstrong, a former member of his survey staff, who was Acting Superintendent of Victoria Hospital in London, Ontario. Mr. Armstrong arrived for an interview. He had taken an officer's course in Kingston during the war; so he was familiar with the city. But the state of the Hospital horrified him. Miss Baillie, Mr. Nickle, and Dr. W. T. Connell were persuasive and greatly influenced his decision to accept the position. He was appointed Superintendent of the Kingston General Hospital to start work 3 March 1925.

Mr. Taylor was persuaded to stay until the end of January when the senior intern, Dr. Stuart Houston, took over as Acting Superintendent until March. Dr. Houston stayed on at the Hospital as chief intern another year because no Queen's graduates were available as interns. Medicine at the University had been changed from a five to a six-year course and that year there was no graduating class. Since the Hospital could not have three Queen's graduates at $50 each, Dr. Houston was rehired at $150.

Fraser Armstrong, having studied Brittain's Report very carefully, was ready to start a vigorous reorganization soon after he took over in March. He wanted to give the staff and patients improved services but at the same time, to put in the badly needed economic controls. The operating deficit had built up to $16,762.21 and there was no provision for depreciation. Hospital accounts were on a cash basis, small purchases made daily, and it was impossible to analyze quickly the state of the finances. Food stuffs had been bought from a different retail grocer each month. That system was immediately changed to wholesale purchasing and within three months the cost of supplies was reduced by over $1,000 a month. Mr. Armstrong and the Board Treasurer set up a new accounting system and consolidated bank accounts and put them in order. By May it was possible to give a clear financial statement and the custom of a monthly financial report was instituted.

Housekeeping was reorganized, a new housekeeper hired and a full-time plumber put on staff to make immediate and necessary repairs. Positions for full-time painter and carpenter were filled next, but a full-time electrician was not considered economical. There was a lot of well-directed activity and a considerable accomplishment in convenience, maintenance, and repair to help staff and patients. The patients benefited further when food carriers and steam tables were bought to improve the Dietary Department.

The new Superintendent was especially good for the Hospital's public relations. Cooperation with people and with governments in the area improved. He made friends with the Women's Aid and, in the interest of good relations with his new housekeeping and dietary staff, persuaded the ladies to change their weekly inspection visits to the occasional conducted tour. He did not manage, however, immediately to persuade the Women's Aid that he could spend their money for linen to better advantage by buying wholesale. That came a year later, following the Hospital's purchase of surplus war material and the acquisition of some linen from the Mowat Hospital. He then suggested other ways in which the ladies might assist the Hospital. Within a few years two sewing groups of the Women's Aid were meeting every week to make uniforms and to sew small garments for the children's wards.

The medical services for patients were greatly improved through the cooperation of the new Superintendent and the Medical Staff in making better use of available funds and facilities. In conference the heads of all the services and Mr. Armstrong reviewed policies, rules, and needs. A pharmacist was engaged to give better, safer and cheaper service in a well organized dispensary. A committee of four surgeons, Austin, Mylks, Bogart, and J. C. Connell, considered the necessary surgical equipment for the new operating rooms, soon to be opened in the Douglas Wing. New rules were made for the use of these rooms, and for control of the equipment, some of which was still privately owned. There was to be no smoking in the operating rooms and the surgeon and his assistants had to wear sterilized gowns. Problems of priorities and scheduling were also considered.

Dr. Etherington chaired a group to correlate the work of the operating rooms and the laboratories. An arrangement was made with Dr. James Miller who agreed to examine all tissues from operations immediately and to report on them. This had been done before mostly on request and for the pay patients. The laboratory work increased to such an extent that Mrs. Richardson's offer in 1927, to pay the salary of a clinical pathologist for five years, was gratefully accepted.

Discoveries and new techniques in blood work brought an offer from the Queen's Medical Faculty in 1926, to help finance the purchase of certain laboratory equipment. The Medical Staff said that facilities for work on blood chemistry were essential if the Hospital was to keep abreast of medical science. And the possibility of such clinical studies was of equal importance to the medical students. Dr. J. F. Logan of Queen's supervised the work in the laboratory, emphasizing the interdependence of teaching, research, and medical care.

All of these things meant more entries on the medical records of the patients, when the doctors could be persuaded to see that the entries were made. In the minutes of a Medical Staff meeting the following entry is typical: 'Dr. Macdonnell made the usual monthly appeal that the members of the staff make a few notes on the hospital records. It was asked particularly that notes on operative findings be made at the time of the operation. As is usual on these occasions the staff was unanimously in accord with this suggestion.'

The single, most spectacular improvement for patients, doctors, and management was celebrated on 16 October 1925, when Dean J. C. Connell officially opened the Richardson Laboratories and the Douglas Wing. The building had public wards on two floors, rooms for tubercular patients, and four operating rooms on the fourth floor. On the first floor there was space for outpatients, X-ray, hydro and light therapy; eye, ear, nose and throat department, electrocardiograph, dispensary, and an office for the Medical Officer of Queen's University. The Pathological Unit became the Pathology Department of Queen's and the Hospital, and also undertook some service for the Department of Public Health. Dean Connell said that it was impossible to estimate what these new facilities would do for the community; the fundamental reason for providing them was the need of the people.

With increased and improved accommodation some of the part-time services had to be made full-time. For example, Dr. R. J. Gardiner and W. E. McNeill of Queen's, serving on the Management Committee, gave strong support to the Medical Staff request for a full-time radiologist. Dr. W. A. Jones, who did his first X-ray work in England in 1919, had been practising his profession as a radiologist in the city. He offered to set up a Radiological and Radio Therapy Department at the Hospital and to take charge of it, provided certain conditions were agreed upon. The Hospital would purchase his office equipment, supply accommodation, light, heat, and laundry free; for this he would give free service to the public ward cases and be available for paid work on a shared fee arrangement. The first charge on fees would be for depreciation of equipment, cost of supplies, repairs, salaries of extra staff, and equipment valuation. The balance was to be divided ninety per cent to the Director of the Department, Dr. Jones, and ten per cent to the Hospital. The service began in January 1926. By March, X-ray began to show a profit and by the end of the year the 1926 receipts had doubled those of 1925. It was a profitable arrangement for both of the partners in the plan.

A committee on anaesthetics – Doctors Austin, Keyes, Mylks, and Angrove – proposed in March 1926, to set up an Anaesthetic Service on much the same basis as for X-ray. The Board, however, did not accept the plan. Dr. Stanley Keyes was then on the Surgical Service in charge of anaesthesia but it was really only a nominal appointment. The majority of anaesthetics were administered by other surgeons or by interns who received little formal clinical instruction. Ether and chloroform were the only anaesthetics in use until ethyl chloride was introduced. In 1929, the Anaesthetic Committee issued a list of precautions and prohibitions: Interns were to use chloroform only under the direction of the surgeon in charge of the operation and the intern must receive special instruction by a member of the

Committee before administering an anaesthetic. The use of the highly flammable ethyl chloride was prohibited, and pre-operative study of the patient was recommended. No further developments in this service came until 1933.

Rapid expansion of medical knowledge made it essential for Kingston General Hospital, as a teaching hospital, to supply facilities to make use of that knowledge. But matters of practical economy forced them to move with cautious speed. Each additional service required more staff, more equipment, more accommodation, and hence more money. Under the new Superintendent's reorganization the nursing staff increased, the laboratory staff grew and there were, in 1926, six junior and three senior interns. In a single month new equipment to the amount of almost $11,000 was approved.

There were new demands on accommodation. In 1925, the Kingston Health Association, operating the Sir Oliver Mowat Memorial Hospital, decided that the twenty-two patients they had were not sufficient for economical operation of a separate tuberculosis hospital. They sold the property to the province the next year to become part of the Rockwood (Psychiatric) Hospital. Of the $150,000 thus realized by the sale, the Health Association agreed to turn over two-thirds to the Kingston General Hospital. On this basis the Kingston General accepted 22 tubercular patients in October 1925.

Balconies were built onto the rear of the Doran Building for the temporary accommodation of these patients. The fourth floor space in the Douglas Wing, designed for such patients, was being used for other patients while Nickle was being renovated. But, although the Hospital felt obligated to operate Douglas IV as a TB unit, that space would not accommodate the 22 patients from the Mowat Hospital. Doran, once the maternity patients had been moved to Nickle, was the only available place for so many patients. Plans were thus made to renovate it. In 1927, the Maternity Department was moved from the Doran Building to its new quarters in the Nickle Wing. Since Doran was to be renovated, the TB patients were moved from the balconies, this time to the Isolation Hospital. That proved to be a satisfactory arrangement and by December 1927 there were only 14 TB patients. Another use could now be found for the Doran Building.

Dr. MacGregor suggested a children's hospital. Dr. Rob Roy MacGregor (Queen's 1916), a native of Brinston, Ontario, who interned at the Hospital for Sick Children in Toronto, came to Queen's in 1923 as a clinical assistant. Ever since his appointment to the Paediatrics staff in 1925, he had been asking for more and better accommodation for children. The Medical Staff persuaded Management to consider the request. In December 1927, the Board accepted a Management recommendation that the Doran Building should be renovated to be used as a children's hospital. The Kiwanis Club and others agreed to help in a canvass for funds to equip the wing and an energetic campaign gained public support. In

April 1929, the Children's Hospital in the Doran Building was officially opened with Dr. MacGregor in charge.

Nurses had already moved into their new home, built on the corner of George and Okill Streets, in front of the 1903 Nurses' Home. The remaining item on the Fifteen Year Plan was the complete renovation of the two oldest buildings, Main and Watkins. In August 1929, after months of consideration of needs and more months of viewing plans and getting estimates, the Building Committee reported to the Board that about $400,000 would be required to rebuild Watkins and Main and to remodel the former nurses' residence on George Street as an internes' quarters, but they made no suggestions regarding the source of funds. The Board of Governors, chaired by H. W. Davis, an extremely practical man, returned the report to the Committee for further study. Dr. J. C. Connell, who had just retired as Dean of the Medical Faculty to be succeeded by Dr. Frederick Etherington, gave up the chairmanship of the Building Committee in disgust and resigned from the Board of Governors. J. M. Campbell was then made chairman but the Board declined to accept Dr. Connell's resignation from the Board. Building plans were soon implemented when the Board received $100,000 from the Ontario government and borrowed another $300,000. The old buildings were vacated, patients, services, and offices distributed throughout the rest of the Hospital and work began by the end of 1929. A year later some space was ready and the remainder was occupied by late spring. The renovated Main and Watkins buildings were opened on Hospital Day, 12 May 1931, to mark the completion of the Fifteen Year Plan. Over $1,500,000 had been contributed and a mortgage of $270,000 remained to be paid.

Expanded accommodation and more and better services requiring a larger staff, brought an increase in the charge for private rooms and for many of the auxiliary services. In the Nickle Wing Maternity Department the most expensive room increased to $6 a day and a semi-private room to $4.50. More babies were born in hospitals although almost forty per cent were still born at home, and it was some time before the Nickle Wing was used to capacity.

The proportion of total revenue from pay patients increased very rapidly and government grants became less important in the total income. In 1928, the provincial grant was increased to sixty cents a day for indigent patients, while the contribution from municipalities was raised to $1.75. Kingston, however, still made a lump sum payment of $12,000, which amounted to about ninety-one cents a day per indigent patient from the City. Since the patient day expense was just over $3.00 the Board of Governors decided that a new agreement should be made with the City to increase their contribution.

The Management Committee reviewed the financial situation. The provincial government made no grants for indigents in the Isolation Hospital, except for tubercular patients, since those with contagious diseases were the sole responsibility of the City. The Board decided to make two proposals to the City: (1) that the City should pay for all indigent patients on the basis of $1.50 a day, or (2) give a lump sum of $12,000 as usual and, in addition, pay the cost of the indigents in the Isolation Hospital. The City chose the second proposal but refused to pay anything for the tubercular patients. In 1926, when asked to increase the lump sum grant to $14,000, the City refused.

Meanwhile Lennox and Addington Counties also made a flat grant; but Frontenac County accepted a $1.50 per diem charge and insisted on proof of residency and indigency. The difficulty of establishing these requirements was a continuing problem. Mr. Armstrong hired a social worker for two months, in 1926, to investigate the residence and financial circumstances of the ward patients. He decided that the expense of the extra worker was not justified and that proof would have to rest on answers to questions asked by the admitting staff of the Hosptial. There were forms and more forms to fill out, not only for the indigents but also for pay patients who could charge to the Workmen's Compensation Board, the Veterans' Administration or to the Queen's Students' Hospital scheme.

The government limitation on the number of days they would pay for any one patient brought an echo of the problem which had plagued the Hospital from the beginning. That problem was the long-time patient who really needed only a good boarding house with minimal nursing care. Mr. Armstrong recommended that all those people not needing regular medical care should be transferred to other institutions; but that was not easily done.

Despite these and other problems, by careful management the Kingston General Hospital had achieved a financial position, especially regarding costs, which was the envy of other institutions and organizations. The Red Cross Society asked permission to study the Hospital's administrative structure, especially the low costs. Five years of stability and strength in management had paid off.

The stock market crash of October 1929, had little immediate effect on the Hospital since there were practically no investments except in a few bequests. Actually 1930 was the year of the highest income and expenditure in the history of the Hospital to that time. Income from pay patients had reached a new peak of $147,229. Then the economic climate affected the Hospital and the period of retrenchment began when income from pay patients dropped $15,000 in one year and continued to decline through 1934. Patients who had once demanded the best accommodation wanted service at a more moderate price; many went into public wards and some simply did not enter hospital at all. In 1934 over sixty-three per cent of the patients were in public wards compared to forty-three per cent in 1929. Private and semi-private service had fallen from fifty-seven to thirty-seven per cent.

In 1932 an operating deficit of over $10,000 was added to the already heavy debt for the new buildings. Collections from patients were falling far behind. R. E.

Burns, Chairman of the Board and an expert in accounting and finance, sought a way to cut the deficit. Various small economies were instituted but there were few not already in effect. There was a change (for Isolation) from a medical prescription of one bottle of whiskey at $4 to one bottle of native wine at eighty cents. Strong evidence of good staff relations and concerned support came when Superintendent Armstrong offered, on the part of the whole Hospital staff, a five per cent donation from the salaries of all executives and employees to help meet the growing deficit. This salary donation was continued to 1938 by a staff grateful for their security while so many others were unemployed.

The Board also acted on a recommendation that they accept fewer probationers in the Training School and keep five members of the graduating class for special post-graduate work. These five graduate nurses were given full maintenance and $30 a month. This scheme provided employment for a few new graduates and supplied better nursing in some critical areas. Under this plan the nurses received special instruction in X-ray, laboratory work and operating room service, rotating in the three services for a year and a half. More graduate nurses were hired for regular staff positions and as assistants. Margaret Blair, a graduate of 1931, became the first graduate assistant to the Operating Room Supervisor, who had used only student nurses before 1932. (When Miss Blair resigned as Operating Room Supervisor in 1948 there were seventeen graduates on the o.r. staff.)

The Hospital wanting to create jobs for unemployed nurses also tried an experiment in special nursing for those who needed, but could not afford, a full-time special nurse. A patient might arrange to have the services of a special nurse for periods ranging from one to four hours instead of the customary twelve-hour service. Four graduate nurses participated in the project but it was discontinued after a trial period, because the nurses were seldom fully employed.

In spite of the depression and the Hospital's financial struggle, the medical, surgical, and supporting services continued to be expanded and improved. It had become apparent that a Department of Urology should be set up at Queen's and at the Hospital to keep up with the progress being made in this speciality. Dr. L. J. Austin, who had become known as one of the best urological surgeons in the area, recommended the establishment of the special department. In 1930, Dr. Nathan E. Berry (Queen's 1926) came from the Royal Victoria Hospital in Montreal to head the department at Queen's and at the Hospital. He had great skill as a surgeon and was a keen clinician and a good teacher. It was a great loss when ill health forced him to give up his practice in 1959.

Recommendations for the appointment of a full-time anaesthetist continued to be made by the Medical Staff. A committee, chaired by Dr. Etherington, made a proposal in 1931, bolstered by statistics to show the need. However, Doctors Keyes, Boucher, and Angrove were giving most of the anaesthetics and the Board decided that funds were not available for a full-time man. It was not until 1934 that Dr. William A. Campbell (Queen's 1924), son of Dr. William Campbell (1861–1923), was brought from the Mayo Clinic in Rochester, Minnesota, to be in charge of the Anaesthetic Division at the Hospital. He brought with him a new anaesthetic, pentothal, which had been introduced experimentally the year before at the Mayo Clinic. Two years later he was put on the instructing staff of the Queen's Faculty of Medicine.

As the Hospital owned no equipment (each anaesthetist used his own) Dr. Campbell had to buy a gas machine to be able to administer cyclopropane which had just come into use. The introduction of spinal anaesthesia a few years later rounded out the sudden emergence of new anaesthetics which contributed so greatly to patient comfort. Dr. Campbell and Dr. Angrove gave free service to ward patients and charged private and semi-private patients a fee. About 1937 the anaesthetic for a tonsillectomy cost $10, or $15 for two members of the same family; for a major operation the charge was $15. A great many of the general practitioners, however, continued for years to administer anaesthetics for minor operations.

There were rapid developments in the field of radiology, especially in the treatment of cancer. Early in 1932 the Board decided to send Dr. W. A. Jones to take a deep-therapy training course, in case a cancer clinic might be established in Kingston. Their preparation was justified when, in September, the Board of Governors and the Medical Staff met to hear a proposal from provincial Health Minister Robb for a Cancer Clinic. The provincial government would give $9,000 a year for ten years and provide the radium if the Hospital would provide the space and administer the Clinic. The proposal was accepted with enthusiasm. The Ontario Institute of Radio Therapy (Kingston Division), one of three in Ontario, was formally opened on 3 March 1933, although it had already been in operation almost a month and had treated thirty-two patients.

But there were serious problems with the early X-ray therapy equipment. The 1934 report of the Kingston Clinic noted that Westinghouse had recently brought out shock-proof equipment which could be purchased for an additional $1,000 beyond credits on the equipment then in use. The acquisition of new equipment continued to be a problem and an expense, as improved machines were rapidly developed.

The Hospital's connection with Queen's gave special help to the Radiology Department. Queen's Professors J. A. Gray and J. K. Robertson, of the Department of Physics, encouraged research in and the teaching of X-ray physics and clinical radiology. In 1930, Queen's began offering a course in Medical Radiology and the men who were trained by Dr. W. A. Jones, the head of that department, became known as 'the Jones' Boys'. One of them, Dr. Ronald W. Burr, joined the department in 1935. Dr. Jones' agreement with the Hospital about the division of earnings was modified to a fifty-fifty basis, instead of the original ninety-ten split, and the Hospital earnings from X-ray grew. By 1939, the Department of Radiology with a staff of seven, plus clerical help, was handling 11,768 cases a year, forty-eight per cent of them free.

A similar split fee arrangement was in effect with Dr. James Miller in Pathology. It gave proof to the wisdom of the general policy of increasing the services offered by the Hospital with as little financial risk as possible to the Hospital. Other services were increased through gifts. Mrs. H. W. Richardson, who died in 1931, left a bequest to the Hospital, announced, in April 1933, as amounting to $100,000. Some of the fund was used to buy an oxygen tent, a McKesson Basal Metabolism apparatus, and a new Cardiograph. Dr. W. T. Connell, executor of the estate, following the wishes of Mrs. Richardson, recommended the establishment of the Alice Ford Richardson Fellowships in Medicine and Surgery, with an independent board to select the recipients.

Dr. Charles Mundell, son of Dr. D. E. Mundell (1864–1923), became the first Richardson Fellow in Surgery and Dr. W. Ford Connell, son of Dr. W. T. Connell, became the first Richardson Fellow in Medicine. Dr. Ford Connell (Queen's 1928) had done postgraduate work in Germany and England in Neurology and Cardiology before he returned to Queen's and the Hospital in 1933. He had four jobs that first year: Richardson Fellow, lecturer in Medicine at Queen's, University Medical Officer, and Registrar of the Ontario Institute of Radio Therapy. The latter job paid him no salary but gave him an office and a secretary.

The next year Dr. Ford Connell became Director of Cardiology. He had two new machines: a mobile cardiograph with heart sound recording and a recording orthodiascope to use in clinical diagnosis. Coronary thrombosis had only recently been recognized as a clinical entity and doctors were just learning how to handle congestive heart failure.

The Chairman of the Board of Governors, J. Stuart Crawford, who suffered from heart trouble, was particularly and personally interested in the development of Dr. Connell's work. Discussions led to the establishment, in January 1938, of a Department of Cardiology at the Hospital and at Queen's with the same financial arrangements as for X-ray. Dr. G. Spencer Melvin became associated with the department. In 1939, the Department of Cardiology reported the increasing use and increasing complexity of examinations and noted that they were making good strides in clinical research. In January 1939, an outpatient heart clinic was opened.

There was, by this time, a whole series of clinics in operation besides the heart clinic – cancer, dental, venereal disease, mental, tuberculosis, and miscellaneous general clinics. They served more than 17,000 patients yearly, not just from

Kingston but from a large surrounding area. The Kingston General Hospital was a regional, not a local, hospital. Fifty per cent of its patients came from an area within twenty-five miles of the Hospital and the other fifty per cent from an area reaching to Toronto, Ottawa, and Montreal.

Every year hospital services increased and costs of hospital care continued to rise. It was a hardship on both the patients and the Hospital which could be eased only by additional funds, and the appeal for gifts was intensified. Dr. M. T. MacEachern, Director of Hospital Services for the American College of Surgeons, reported in June 1934: 'Kingston General Hospital is one of the best equipped, organized and managed institutions on this continent and worthy of the full confidence of any benefactor. I cannot speak too highly of this institution.' Unfortunately not many benefactors came forward in the depression era and there could be no certainty of such a source of income.

The decrease in pay patient income between 1930 and 1934 alarmed the Hospital administrators who saw the one source of income under their control dwindling rapidly. These funds that were used to cover losses on indigent service, were in danger of disappearing. There was a growing feeling that the man of moderate means who could not really afford hospital care and did not want to accept charity was bearing the brunt. It was important to devise a programme for more adequate distribution of hospital costs.

Such a distribution was in effect in the Queen's Student Health scheme with the Hospital which started in 1903. It had developed over the years so that all Queen's Students paid a regular, modest fee to entitle them to hospital care and the Hospital had a regular, if small, income from this plan. In 1933, Management considered a similar scheme which would be open to public school teachers in Kingston. Out of the discussions which followed that proposal a larger plan emerged.

Superintendent Armstrong presented to the Board of Governors in January 1934, what he called a Community Cooperative Group Hospital Plan. It received rapid approval of the Board, chaired at that time by W. T. Minnes. On May 12, National Hospital Day, it was announced to the public and the subscription list was opened. By closing date, the middle of June, a total of 380 subscriptions were in and the list was held open for another few days. The annual fee was so small that almost anyone could afford to belong. The schedule set forth a fee of $5 for an individual, plus $2 for a wife and $1 for each other member of the family. It was really aimed at the low income person who had to go into debt to pay hospital bills or who, perhaps, refused to go into hospital because he could not afford it. The plan assisted but did not relieve the patient of all responsibility for payment of hospital bills.

The financial solvency of the plan was assured by collecting the fees in advance and providing for payment on a reimbursement concept. About one half of the hospital bill paid by a member of the plan at either the Kingston General Hospital or the Hotel Dieu was returned. The first benefit came when a member paid his hospital bill. A family, within the fiscal year, was entitled to a fifteen-day credit, with a maximum to any one person of ten days, at a rate of $2.50 a day for any regular-priced service, private or semi-private. When the plan started, the basic cost of a semi-private room was only $2.50 a day.

Families eligible for public ward service and paying for it, were entitled to a twenty-day credit with a maximum to any one person of fifteen days at the public ward pay rate of $1.75 a day. The deferred benefit came at the end of the year when the relation of the total cost to the total income was computed on a percentage basis and further benefits were distributed. At the end of the first year about forty-six per cent of the cost of hospital bills had been returned to subscribers.

The publicity attendant on the success of the plan convinced the 'wait and see' public of the value of the Kingston Community Plan. In the second year there were 943 subscribers and over the seven years the plan was in existence it grew to cover over 3,000 persons. The average fee paid per person in 1938 was $2.75, making hospital service more economically available to the eighty per cent of pay patients who had only moderate incomes. Of course, Hospital charges had increased: the semi-private room which had been cut to $2.50 in 1934 had reached $3 a day by 1938. Private rooms ranged from $3.50 to $7, with increased charges for diagnostic and supporting services.

Income from pay patients had again become the major source of revenue for the Hospital. That was a fortunate situation since the provincial government developed closer controls on payments for the indigent patients, and the municipal government was often in arrears in its obligations. Increase in the government per diem grant fell far behind the increase in costs. When a period of severe unemployment came in the mid 1930s there was a strain on public ward facilities as families could not afford private or semi-private rooms.

The provincial and federal governments asked for more proof of indigency and more reports on patients eligible for hospital grants. In October 1933, the Hospital faced a problem in attempting to recover the cost of treatment for patients from the camp for the unemployed. They were non-residents and no government was prepared to accept the responsibility for their hospital bills. As the bills for indigents rose, more government controls were imposed. The province, not satisfied with local decisions on eligibility for free care, asked the Hospital to submit a financial report on each patient receiving free service.

Local governments also made new regulations. The Counties of Lennox and Addington directed the Hospital to accept no indigent patient from those counties except those authorized by a Mayor or a Reeve. The indigents from Ernestown were to be admitted only on the order of the Health Officer or the township would not pay the bill. The admitting officer faced problems both economic and humane.

Kingston continued to use the lump sum payment, plus a grant for the Isolation Hospital. But in 1934 the payment for the Isolation Hospital was more than twelve months in arrears. In 1936, the City's total grant to the Hospital had reached $20,000 but was not enough to cover the costs of all indigent patients from the City. Some new arrangement was necessary. The Hospital proposed, in 1937, that the $20,000 from the City would be taken as payment for patient days at statutory rates; the $20,000 would pay for 12,000 patient days. If the cost of caring for City indigents was less than that sum the City would get a rebate; if it was over $20,000 the City would pay the Hospital fifty cents per patient day over the flat sum.

Superintendent Armstrong thought that, although this plan gave the City an incentive to exercise reasonable control on the number of indigent patients sent to the Hospital, it was not so drastic as to decrease the usefulness of the Hospital to the community. Within a year after the plan was accepted the number of indigent patients from the City was reduced. This was partly because the City was making a closer check on them, partly because the doctors could get payment for office service to indigents. In 1939, the Ontario government asked indigent patients who could, to pay $2.35 per day to the hospital for the first five days, instead of the $1.75 asked before. The Kingston General Hospital had experienced some difficulty in collecting even the $1.75 and thought that different arrangements should be made. The Superintendent said that it was the Hospital's duty to render a service rather than act as a collecting agency for the municipality.

Government supervision of patient welfare through grants, reports, and inspections was also carried over into staff welfare. The Provincial Inspector, at one time, criticized the state of the nurses' dining room. In 1938, he said that two more nurses should be hired for night duty to provide for rest periods for the night nurses. There were also official regulations about the number of nurses who must be on staff in tubercular treatment centres supported by the government. More graduate nurses had to be hired for the TB floor in the Isolation Hospital.

By 1939 there were forty-one graduate nurses on the staff at the Kingston General Hospital, including the eight in Isolation. And there were 120 student nurses doing general duty throughout the Hospital. Pay for graduates had increased and discussions had started about a possible change from the twelve hour shift to an eight hour shift. The change was instituted first only for special nurses, then for graduate nurses.

In 1933 there had been consideration of a pension plan for employees, and discussions on it reopened in 1937. Statistics were compiled on the length of service and the age of every Hospital employee, in order to compute the possible costs. The expense of providing a pension plan, even with strict limitations, was estimated at $585 a month. A full plan was beyond the financial ability of the Hospital but a start had to be made. Management recommended that $200 a month should be put into a special fund and that each retirement should be considered separately. In April 1936, the Board, under Chairman R. G. H. Travers, had provided for sickness leave and a retirement pension of $60 a month for Miss Emma Hunter. She had been on the Hospital staff since 1899, and she returned after her sick leave to do some light duties until her final illness and death in 1958.

The Fifteen Year building plan was completed in 1931. Six years later the expanded services and increasing numbers of patients made the planning for further physical expansion mandatory. A special committee on long range needs was formed and directed to consider the joint requirements of the Hospital, Queen's and the Medical Staff. One of the immediate considerations was a query from Queen's about the proper site for a new biochemistry building, the gift of Dr. Agnes Douglas Craine who had graduated from Queen's in 1888. It would contain laboratories serving both Queen's and the Hospital. The Craine Building was erected at the eastern side of the medical quadrangle on the Queen's campus, and Dr. Gordon Sinclair became the Craine Professor of Biochemistry.

The first report of this joint survey committee dealt with policies and facilities. They said that the administrative and physical structure was ideal for a broad development of Hospital work, in conjunction with Queen's Medical School, to promote the Hospital as a referral centre. They recommended the expansion of such revenue producing services as the Cancer Clinic and the Urological Department. They mentioned the space needs of X-ray, the laboratories, the Dietary Department, and the lack of adequate accommodation for interns, nurses, and help. They drew attention to the problem of transportation within the Hospital with the maze of long corridors, and the need for more elevators. In their opinion the Nickle Wing and the fourth floor of the Douglas Wing were too small for efficient and economical administration. The Doran Building, they said, was inadequate in many ways, especially as a children's hospital.

At the 1938 annual meeting, when Prof. Manly B. Baker became Chairman of the Board of Governors, it was decided that a new children's unit would be a fitting centenary commemoration for 1945. The Board decided, also, that since such a unit would probably be operated at a loss, it should have at least $125,000 for an endowment. That was in addition to the $75,000 they estimated would be required to build the new unit and to renovate Doran. The quarterly meeting of the Board in May 1939 noted progress in plans for the promotion of the new building. Then came World War II.

Eight

Great Britain declared war on Germany 3 September 1939; one week later Canada also declared war. With no strong dramatic leader and no immediate national danger Canada seemed engaged at first in a moderate official war effort. There was initially only limited mobilization but over 58,000 men volunteered in the first month of the war. Conscription troubles were to begin later.

World War II and the Victory Progress Plan 1940–1949

Severe Allied reverses in 1940, with Dunkirk and the French collapse, changed the feelings and the policy in Canada. Furthermore, the thousands of young men brought to this country under the British Commonwealth Air Training Plan inspired Canadians to a greater war effort in both enlistments and in the national economy. The National Resources Mobilization Act of June 1940 initiated a sudden and large expansion of Canadian war industries affecting all parts of the country.

Kingston changed rather quickly from a quiet military, educational, and service centre to a busy industrial city. Within two years the Aluminum Company and Canadian Industries, Ltd. each had a huge plant in operation at Kingston. The older industrial firms in the city responded to the economic mobilization; the Locomotive Works and the Kingston Shipyards were soon in full war production. Expanded industries quickly absorbed the available labour force and offered high wages to entice workers from rural areas and from other jobs.

The civilian war effort in Kingston was overshadowed by Kingston's historic role as a garrison town. Many military groups mustered in Kingston as it became headquarters of Military District No. 3. The Navy at H.M.C.S. Cataraqui and the Air Force at the Norman Rogers Field added to the service force in and near the city. And, as in other war times, large number of dependents of the service men settled in the city for the duration of the war. Kingston's civilian population increased by about 13,000 and caused a severe housing shortage.

There were other shortages all over the country. Limited rationing in Canada came to an abrupt end with Pearl Harbour and from early 1942 there was strict coupon rationing of gasoline and of various foodstuffs. Production of civilian garments and domestic furnishings was curtailed as factories converted to war needs. Prices of everything rose rapidly until controls were imposed by the Wartime Prices and Trades Board. During the rest of World War II the cost of living rose only about a further twenty per cent compared to over fifty per cent in the first World War.

The lessons learned from that first War were very much in the minds of the Management Committee of the Kingston General Hospital when Chairman M. B. Baker called them to a special meeting on 18 September 1939. They approved Superintendent Armstrong's plan to purchase and stockpile certain essential medical supplies. It was a wise decision, for by January 1940, many of those supplies cost sixty per cent more. By the following June the cost of some surgical supplies had gone up almost 200 per cent.

The Committee surveyed the available accommodation in the Hospital and considered transferring patients from one floor to make it ready for military patients should an emergency arise. They noted that the City was talking about closing the Isolation Hospital, now usually more than half empty. But by the end of 1939 every Hospital bed was full.

Management decided that as part of their war effort they would offer surgical training to a limited number of graduate nurses who intended to enlist. That kind of war effort tended to expand even without official sanction. Within a year Superintendent Armstrong reported that the Kingston General Hospital seemed to be serving as a training centre for special military nurses, orderlies, cooks, and technicians. There was a constant turnover and consequently a shortage of trained and untrained personnel at the Hospital. By the end of 1942, only five of the fifty graduate nurses who had been on the payroll in 1939 were still at the Hospital.

At that first special meeting Dr. W. A. Jones informed the Committee that he was leaving to be Consultant Radiologist to the Director General of Medical Services for the Canadian Active Service Force. He advised the Committee to find an assistant for Dr. R. C. Burr at the Hospital, or perhaps two, especially if Dr. Burr also might be called up. But the Canadian medical profession had learned a lesson from the last war when civilian medical services were jeopardized and medical training was disrupted by the uncontrolled enlistment of doctors. The Canadian Medical Association undertook immediately to make a register of all medical men in Canada, indicating what contribution each could make to the war. This register was completed in 1940 and was of great value to the Department of Defence. The Medical Association also set up a Medical Advisory Committee to work with divisional committees in meeting military and civilian medical needs. Thus the war hastened the movement, already under way, to national standards and professional cooperation. The intern appointments at the Kingston General Hospital in 1939 were the first they made in cooperation with the Canadian Intern Board.

Other medical programmes which had received grudging support were soon considered to be wartime priorities. Research to save lives received its greatest financial assistance and encouragement during the war. The 1938 Banting survey of research facilities and resources in Canadian medical schools supplied much basic information for part of the wartime grants programme for medical research. Tremendous advances in medical knowledge and techniques had been made since World War I when, for instance, there had been practically no medical treatment for bacterial infection. The sulfonamides, introduced in the late 1930s, were proving almost miraculous in controlling such infections. Penicillin, brought into use about the time of the invasion of Normandy, was a real miracle drug with fewer side effects.

These life-saving drugs were not, of course, limited to battle casualty use. The sulfa drugs had already decreased the number of days most patients stayed in hospital. There was, however, a marked increase in the number of patients and in the intensity of treatment, with a consequent increase in cost to the Hospital. New drugs and new equipment cost more, and additional staff, both nursing and technical, were required to administer and control the new treatments. Trained personnel were at a premium, even before the war.

The attraction of higher pay in war industries had to be offset by raises in all salaries at the Hospital. As the basic government grants had not increased, these added costs were met with some small increases in room and service charges. An increase of twenty-five cents a day in a few room rates brought objections from some of the Medical Staff. They were told that medical men should not try to dictate the price of rooms any more than the Hospital Superintendent should tell doctors what to charge a patient. With the booming wartime economy the cost of patient care was not nearly so critical as the shortage of accommodation. Each year the patient-day service at the Hospital reached a new high.

Kingston General Hospital's special survey committee, which had been working since 1937, was very much aware of the needs. However, with a war economy, they could do little but make long range plans to deal later with the acute need for expansion. In a pamphlet dated 31 December 1942, the Committee of Management announced a Ten-Year Plan. The annual meeting of the Board of Governors in March 1943, approved the plan to accumulate a fund of about $800,000 to expand the Kingston General Hospital to a six-hundred-bed, teaching hospital with adequate supporting services. The priorities, as first announced, were for expanded facilities for out-patients, laboratory, and teaching, additional accommodation for nurses, space for one hundred and eighty new beds, an extension to the Dietary Department, a new Maternity Wing, and the fire-proofing of the old Doran Wing.

The twenty-five per cent increase in maternity cases in the first year of the war emphasized the need for more beds in that service. Dr. G. W. Mylks, Sr. had, for some time, complained about the inadequate, inconvenient, and inefficient maternity accommodation. In the Nickle Wing only twenty-six beds could be set up on the four floors. The government regulations regarding nursing care forced the Hospital to assign a disproportionate number of student and graduate nurses to that service at a time when nurses were in short supply.

Increased population, crowded home conditions, and the various hospital insurance and assistance plans all contributed to the pressure on Kingston Hospital accommodation. The federal government set up a plan to help service men's families meet hospital costs. However, some soldiers' dependents did not make proper applications for assistance and, by 1942, the Kingston General Hospital counted over $6,000 in unpaid bills for them. The Kingston Community Plan, though it brought an increased number of local citizens to Hospital, did assure prompt payment. The Ontario Plan for Hospital Care, which began in 1941, covered over 9,000 people in the Kingston area in the first year and over 19,000 by 1944.

The pressure on the Hospital facilities was tremendous. At times of peak capacity, corridors and sunrooms had to be used as wards. There were seldom fewer than thirty military patients at the Kingston General Hospital. In 1940, the Management Committee suggested that a special section might be built for them by adding a fifth floor to the Watkins Wing. That problem was settled in July 1941, when the War Services Commission took over the buildings of St. Mary's of the Lake Orphanage for use as a separate military hospital. The service men's dependents, however, still had to use the Kingston General Hospital and Hotel Dieu.

The military continued to make use of many of the special services at the Kingston General Hospital, especially those conducting the medical tests for tuberculosis and venereal disease. In January 1940, the Provincial Department of Health had set up, in cooperation with the Hospital, a Fever Therapy Unit to treat neurosyphilitic cases. Dr. Berry was in charge of that Unit as well as of the Department of Urology.

The work of the Radiology Department, under Dr. R. C. Burr, put a burden not only on the smaller staff but also on the equipment. A new power supply had to be installed so that both X-ray rooms could be used simultaneously. And with the ten-year provincial grant for the Institute of Radio Therapy due to run out in 1942 there was considerable concern over continued government support.

Similar conditions prevailed in other services. The steadily mounting work in Cardiology curtailed their research projects which were further hampered by constantly changing technicians and Residents. Some laboratory work for the Army was moved to the Provincial Health Laboratory on Barrie Street. The need for more biochemistry tests was met by contracting with Prof. Gordon Sinclair to do the tests at the Craine Building at Queen's. A Blood Bank, set up in November 1942, put a further strain on accommodation.

More laboratory space, more operating rooms and a bigger Out-patient Department could not be put off until after the war. In 1942, the Board approved the construction of additions to meet those immediate needs. The extension to the sterilization and operating rooms on the roof of the Douglas Wing brought another problem. Some old and overworked equipment, such as the sterilizer which had been purchased at the close of World War I had to be replaced. Mrs. Thelma Boucher presented a new sterilizer section as a memorial to her father, Dr. Gordon Bogart (Queen's 1901), a surgeon who had been associated with the Hospital for almost forty years.

To maintain high standards of efficiency and service under war-time conditions required the utmost cooperation of everyone connected with the Hospital and put an added burden on many of the volunteer workers. The Chairman of the Board of Governors during the war years, each of whom served for two years, were: Prof. Manly Baker, 1939; E. W. Waldron, 1941; and Elmer Davis, 1943. They also served as Chairmen of the Management Committee, and were usually in daily conference with the Superintendent on Hospital problems. In 1941, two members of the Women's Aid became members of the Board of Governors, giving official voice to the large and active group of women volunteers who were giving extra time and help to the Hospital.

Miss Olevia Wilson was appointed Assistant Superintendent in 1940, recognizing by title the work she had been doing for some time. The Superintendent's problems in securing supplies and personnel became even more difficult as the war continued. William Grant, Head Pharmacist, left and was succeeded by his assistant, Fred Buck, who carried a heavy work load with a diminished staff. Miss Annie Potter, Chief Dietitian, retired because of illness in 1942. One day in that year over half of the dietary staff left for war service, complicating an already difficult situation.

The nursing staff underwent the greatest changes, especially in the first three years of the war. Miss Mabel Bonter, who had served as a Supervisor for fifteen years, retired in 1940. The staff was greatly depleted by early enlistments and replacements were hard to find. Superintendent of Nurses Anne Baillie obtained permission in that year to hire a married nurse, something that had never been done since the Training School started.

In July 1941, Miss Baillie was seriously ill. She died in February 1942, after eighteen years as Superintendent of Nurses, serving the Hospital with devotion and distinction. She had taken over the Nurses' Training School when it was at such a low ebb that it had been removed from the approved list. Under her supervision it was reorganized in a short time to become an excellent, approved school with high standards and a steadily growing student body. She had developed the nursing staff at the Hospital from three graduate nurses in 1924 to fifty-five graduates just before the war. It was Miss Baillie's recommendation, put into effect after her death, which instituted the first full-time night staff of operating room nurses. The day staff in the operating rooms had increased from one graduate to eight. In 1944, Miss Evelyn Freeman, who had been for twenty-three years the Chief Operating Room Nurse, resigned. Miss Margaret Blair, her assistant for twelve years, became Head Nurse in the Operating Room Section.

Miss Louise Acton, who had been Chief Instructor of Nurses since 1924, became Superintendent of Nurses. A series of instructors took over her duties in the Training School. The pressure on the nursing staff had increased to such an extent that more help in their less specialized tasks had to be found. For some years there had been a few nurses' aides, one in the operating room, one on each public floor and one in maternity. From the beginning of the war a few volunteers, mostly soldiers' wives, served as nurses' aides in the evening. The success of these assistants, both paid and volunteer, in relieving the nurses of minor duties led to a formal training programme. In the spring of 1943, a class for nurses' aides began with nineteen girls taking classes for a month before they began practical work. The course was that given for VAD work in the army and trained the girls for 'lesser nursing duties' to relieve nurses for more expert patient care. By 1944 there were thirty trained aides on duty at the Hospital, supplying relief at a critical time. Since then their training and usefulness have increased.

The Medical Staff at the Hospital lost a few senior men to the services during the war but lost more through death or retirement. Dr. W. T. Connell, at age sixty-seven, had been called up as Medical Consultant to Military District No. 3. His son, Dr. Ford Connell, took his place as Acting Head of the Department of Medicine at Queen's University and at the Hospital. Dr. Ford Connell became Head in 1943, but, since he was also Head of Cardiology and doing some work in neurology, he insisted on having a full-time Assistant Head of Medicine. He was assisted by Dr. Gordon Cornett in 1943 and by Dr. G. K. Wharton from 1944 to 1946.

Dr. Edwin Robertson arrived in 1939 to be Head of the Department of Obstetrics and Gynaecology of the Queen's Medical Faculty. In 1940, he succeeded Dr. Gordon Mylks, Sr., as Head of that service at the Hospital. Dr. Robertson, a native of Edinburgh, Scotland, received his medical training at the University of

Edinburgh and at Lausanne University. Most of the changes he recommended in the Hospital Maternity Department had to be delayed because of war-time priorities.

In Surgery there were many staff changes. Dr. Frederick Etherington left the Hospital staff of Surgery in 1943. He retired as Dean of the Faculty of Medicine at Queen's and was succeeded there by Dr. G. Spencer Melvin. Dr. L. J. Austin, Head of Surgery, became ill in 1944 and died 20 March 1945. The Kingston General Hospital annual report for 1944, printed early in 1945, listed only three men in Surgery: Dr. Duncan W. Boucher, Dr. Stuart W. Houston, both also on the Queen's staff, and a clinical assistant, Dr. G. C. Lindsay. Queen's had begun to look for a new Chief of Surgery in 1943 but no appointment was made until 1945.

Other areas had similar staff problems. The Mental Health Clinic from the first had difficulty in keeping a Director. Doctors A. M. Doyle, S. G. Chalk, K. M. McGregor, and C. A. Bright followed in quick succession. As it was impossible to find a replacement in 1944, Dr. C. H. McCuaig, the Superintendent of Rockwood Psychiatric Hospital, became Acting Director until the end of the war.

The Chest Clinic, set up in 1937, was fortunate in retaining Dr. Bruce Hopkins as Director and in securing the assistance of the Kingston Medical Officer of Health and of the Public Health Nurse. Dr. Hopkins had been Medical Director of the Sir Oliver Mowat Hospital from 1917 to 1925 and then served as Director of the TB wards at the Kingston General Hospital. The Medical Staff had always felt that patients with tuberculosis should be treated in a separate hospital. With the long bed care and minimal treatment it was uneconomic to continue to use Hospital beds which were badly needed for more intensive treatment of other diseases. The Ontario government, under pressure to provide sanatoria for the TB patients, gave serious consideration to possible sites. In March 1944, Kingston was chosen as one site. But Ongwanada Sanatorium did not open until August 1948, in a building on Princess Street, built to house female industrial workers during the war. Dr. Bruce Hopkins served as Medical Director of Ongwanada from 1948 through 1970.

Pressures from inside and from outside the Hospital brought new problems in medicine and in administration. A Medical-Administrative Conference Committee was set up in 1943 to improve communication and to strengthen the formal co-operation of the Medical Staff and the Hospital administration. One of their persistent problems for a good many years was provision of office space in the Hospital for members of the Queen's Medical Faculty. The heads of the medical departments at Queen's were also heads of the corresponding services at the Hospital, as was the custom in major teaching hospitals. They needed to be available not only for teaching but also for Hospital service and consequently occupied office space in the Hospital. Some of the other doctors complained that these men, making use of their Hospital offices for private consultations and referrals, enjoyed an unfair advantage over other staff doctors. Concurrently there were problems regarding clinical teaching material and some criticism of the policies of the Chiefs of Staff. In 1943, the Board recommended that the staff offices at the Hospital not be used for any private professional practice but the motion could not be implemented until many years later. Meanwhile the Hospital built more offices along the west side of the corridor between Main and Empire to accommodate the doctors on the teaching and attending staff.

The Medical Conference Committee dealt also with problems concerning interns' duties and responsibilities, their holidays and working and living conditions. They made rules for the use of laboratory and auxiliary services and specified the charges to be made for such services. They also examined and agreed on new medical procedures to be used at the Hospital. And to further the interests of both of their employers, they encouraged the formation of a joint policy committee for Queen's and the Hospital. It was imperative, they said, to recognize the interdependence of the Hospital and the Medical Faculty in securing funds and in planning future expansion.

What became known as the 'Victory Progress Plan' had been conceived in 1942 as the Ten-Year Plan. The expansion of facilities was to be undertaken in units as funds became available. The scope of that plan increased in years and in costs as new needs were considered. The Governors envisaged a fifteen or even, possibly, a fifty-year plan. The estimated total funds needed for the definite projects rose from $787,000 in January 1943 to $1,800,000 in 1944.

It had become increasingly evident by 1944 that some of the planned expansion could not wait for the end of the war. The ten-year provincial grant (1932–1942) for the Institute of Radio Therapy had been extended to cover 1943 and was renewed for 1944. Future grants depended on the results of a government survey, a study which showed serious space problems for the Institute. Patients had to wait in the hallway; there was not enough room for files; and it was practically impossible to carry on the teaching work of the Institute in such cramped quarters. The provincial government was considering the establishment of Cancer Clinics and the Kingston General Hospital, because of the excellent work of Dr. R. C. Burr, was a likely location for one of them, but only if adequate space could be found.

That space had to be found, not in ten or fifteen years, but quickly if Kingston was to get the clinic. Dr. W. T. Connell, Chairman of the Victory Progress Plan Committee, had approved the idea of a long range building plan but insisted that the immediate needs had to be met. He said that a five-year plan should provide more beds for civilian and for military patients as well as better equipment and space for teaching and for clinical work.

So, while the long range plans were being formulated, the Board of Governors decided to seek funds for an immediate further extension to the Empire Wing. The Department of Pensions and National Health made a proposal regarding funds. This department, formed in 1928 by a merger of the Department of Health and the Department of Soldiers Civil Re-establishment, was in the process of re-organization in 1944 and by the end of the year it had split to become the Department of National Health and Welfare and the Department of Veterans' Affairs. In August 1944, the Board met to discuss the proposed contract which assured to the Hospital building fund a government grant of $100,000. In turn, the Hospital had to give the Department admission priorities to at least eighty beds. A further capital grant from the province depended on the provision of special and expensive laboratory facilities. The extension to the Empire Wing had been estimated at $250,000 in 1943. The estimate had risen to $325,000 within a year and reached $475,000 when tenders were called in April 1945. But the Hospital had to meet its commitments. Shortly after the surrender of Germany on 7 May 1945, Dr. W. T. Connell announced a public campaign to raise $300,000 to assist in building the extension to the Empire Wing. It would be called the Victory Wing. On 24 May the first sod was turned. On 6 August, His Excellency Viscount Alexander laid the cornerstone. In spite of shortages of material and labour the Wing was in use the next year in time to accommodate veterans who had to be moved to Kingston after a fire at the Peterborough Hospital.

The ground floor of the new Victory Wing was designed to meet the needs of cancer treatment. In December 1945, the Minister of Health and the officials of the Cancer Foundation announced that the first Cancer Clinic in Ontario would be opened in the Kingston General Hospital early in 1947. The Foundation supplied the furniture and professional equipment. The members of staff were named by the Queen's Medical Faculty and appointed by the Cancer Foundation. Dr. R. C. Burr was put in charge of the Clinic. All methods of diagnosis and therapy were included in the one organization in their new quarters.

Victory Wing had four floors for patients. The rooms were designed for fairly flexible use; they could be used as private or semi-private accommodation. Some of the rooms were equipped to take three beds if more beds were needed. Eighty of the new beds in the Victory Wing had to be available for veterans, admitted under the contract with the government.

Although the war's end lifted official restrictions on construction, the shortage of funds and of materials exercised a strong unofficial restriction. An addition to the Hospital laundry building was finished early in 1948 but the necessary machinery was slow in delivery. Prices continued to rise; the proposed expansion, renovation, and improvements to the Hospital were estimated to total about $3,000,000.

The end of the war had some results more positive and happy for the Hospital and the Queen's Medical Faculty. The Medical Staff, diminished by death, retirement, and war service, welcomed back former colleagues and some new staff members. Dr. W. A. Jones returned to the Radiology Department early in October 1945. Dr. Burr was then able to concentrate on radio therapy and cancer treatment. Dr. D. L. C. Bingham arrived from Edinburgh late in 1945 to become Head of the Department of Surgery at Queen's and head of that service at the Hospital. Dr. Bingham graduated from the Medical School of Edinburgh University in 1934 and did graduate work in London, Vienna, Ann Arbor and in Scotland. A vigorous reorganization of the operating room schedules, supplies, procedures and staff responsibilities began under the direction of Doctors Berry, Bingham, and Edwin Robertson.

In Medicine Dr. G. Malcolm Brown (Queen's 1938) returned to Kingston after three years of clinical and research work in London and a further three years with the Malaria Research Unit of the R.A.M.C. He replaced Dr. Wharton as assistant to Dr. Ford Connell and his activities were divided among research, teaching, and clinical work. A year later, 1947, Dr. Denis Naldret White, trained at Cambridge and London, joined the expanding medical staff to relieve Dr. Ford Connell of the work in Neurology. Meanwhile the Mental Health Clinic, after two years of very curtailed activity, had been reorganized in February 1946 with Dr. R. M. Billings (Queen's and Toronto) as Director.

The Laboratory Service had improved under the supervision of Dr. J. T. Tweddell but he wished to be relieved of this extra work which he had agreed to do only temporarily. Dr. John Hamilton was brought from Montreal in 1946 to be Head of the Pathology Department and Chief of Laboratory Services. Dr. W. D. Hay (Queen's 1921) continued as Associate in the department. Doctors G. B. Reed and John Orr did the work in Bacteriology and Doctors R. G. Sinclair and Eldon Boyd in Biochemistry. Dr. E. P. White (Queen's 1934), whose special training in Urology at the Royal Victoria Hospital had been interrupted by the war, returned in 1946 to assist Dr. N. E. Berry.

Dr. W. A. Campbell, who had come to the Hospital in 1934, was made Head of Anaesthesiology at Queen's in 1945 and chief of that service at the Hospital. Dr. Angrove and Dr. Milligan were his associates. Dr. H. P. Folger, who had recently been appointed Professor of Ophthalmology and chief of the newly established Eye Department at the Hospital, died in November 1946, after almost twenty years' service at Kingston General Hospital. His place was taken by Dr. J. G. McBroom (Queen's 1934) and Dr. G. B. Macpherson (Queen's 1937) who were added to Dr. F. A. Cays's department of Eye, Ear, Nose and Throat. The first Ophthalmologist at the Hospital, Dr. James Connell, former Dean of Medicine and Chairman of the Board of Governors, died in October 1947.

In 1949 the Hospital, Queen's University, and the medical profession suffered two serious losses. In August, Dr. R. Gordon Sinclair, Craine Professor of Bio-chemistry, died in a drowning accident. He had gained an international reputation for his contribution to the knowledge of lipid metabolism. A month later Dr. G. Spencer Melvin died after a long illness. Coming to Queen's and the Hospital in 1919, he had served with distinction as Professor of Physiology and Dean of the Faculty of Medicine.

Dr. G. Harold Ettinger (Queen's 1920) became Dean of Medicine in 1949. Dr. Ettinger had been research assistant in the Banting and Best Department of Medical Research in Toronto and his interest in continuing research encouraged his colleagues at both Queen's and the Hospital. He had a long and outstanding connection with the Medical Research Council.

During the war and for a short time afterward the placing of interns was controlled by the Army Medical Service. The Kingston General Hospital Medical Conference Committee noted, in February 1946, that the Medical Officer of District No. 3 had detailed fourteen graduates of Queen's Faculty of Medicine to intern at the Hospital. The Medical Staff wanted more interns, especially more seniors, but the Hospital budget allowed only $18,000 for seventeen interns and one supervisor. This sum had to cover fees, maintenance, bonus, and incidentals. The maintenance cost of an intern for one month was estimated as:

90 meals @ 30¢	$27
Room at $2 a week	8
Laundry & uniforms	12
Miscellaneous	3
	$50

Interns asked for an increase in their 'honoraria' and the Medical Staff recommended that the senior interns' salary be increased by $25 a month. Something had to be done to attract the best men as the war had kept the supply of interns from meeting the demands of the enlarging services in Canadian hospitals. When the intern staff could not be filled at the Hospital in 1946, the Medical Staff, reconsidering an earlier decision not to hire a woman intern, decided to recommend the appointment of Dr. Charlotte Ferencz, if suitable accommodation for her could be found. Women were accepted as interns but a certain resistance to their presence was still evident. For instance, in 1948, the Genito-Urinary Service at the Hospital decided to dispense with the services of female interns, but agreed to put on a demonstration monthly to help in their training.

In the next few years it became even more difficult to fill the intern posts although an increasing number of young doctors from abroad were coming to Canadian hospitals. In one year the Kingston General Hospital had over fifty applications from overseas. Transportation difficulties made such appointments precarious.

There were often months when the intern service was very short staffed, awaiting arrival of new interns from overseas.

There were some differences among departments in the Hospital, in the methods of appointment and in the grades of interns. In the fall of 1948, the Medical Conference Committee set the policy regarding appointments, control and procedures for Junior Interns, Senior Interns, Fellows, Clinical Tutors, and Research Officials. Some interns held two positions; for instance, in Obstetrics the Senior Intern was also appointed Clinical Tutor so that the additional salary could attract a graduate of better quality. In Anaesthesia Dr. W. A. Campbell had been asking for a Senior rather than a Junior Rotating Intern who would be with him only a short time. The first such appointment was made in May 1949, when Dr. James Mahood (Queen's 1947) was appointed Clinical Tutor and Senior Intern in Anaesthetics. In 1949, CAMSI, the Canadian Association of Medical Students and Interns, set up a placement service and the Kingston General Hospital entered into an agreement with them to conform to national standards and procedures in intern appointments.

The shortage of graduate nurses during the war carried over into peacetime when it was still very difficult to get Supervisors. The Hospital had raised wages but could not yet provide accommodation for the complete nursing staff. In June 1946, when the Hospital Training School for Nurses celebrated its 60th year, there were 138 students on a nursing staff totalling 261. Miss Louise Acton, Superintendent of Nurses, spoke to the Medical Conference Committee. She said that the Kingston General Hospital must institute an eight-hour day, six-day week, and a pension scheme if they were to get and to keep good nurses. At that time only the eight operating room nurses and one nurse on each floor were on an eight-hour shift. All others were still working twelve hours.

In 1947, an eight-hour, six-day week was in effect for all graduate nurses at the Hospital, but not yet for all students. There were 307 on the nursing staff, the increase needed to achieve the eight-hour day. Forty of the staff were nurses' aides, who, trained in a government approved course, were able to relieve the nursing staff of many less important duties. The Governors bought Calvin House, on King Street near the Hospital, as a residence for the graduate nurses but many of them still had to find rooms in town.

Student nurses also had accommodation problems. The Training School was in need of better and larger quarters to care for the largest class in the history of the School. They also needed improved teaching facilities to maintain the educational standards of the School. At Queen's nursing was given formal recognition as a subject of study with the introduction, in 1946, of a course leading to the degree of Bachelor of Nursing Science. Miss Dorothy Riches, Director of the School at

Queen's, was made welcome by the Hospital School and worked cooperatively with staff and students.

Throughout the war there had been a persistent problem with help in various services at the Hospital. Dietitians came and went almost yearly until Miss Virginia Hess took charge in 1946. But kitchen help, like all other help, was difficult to get even after the war, until wages were increased sharply and a pension plan for employees was adopted. Other staff benefits were instituted to satisfy current demands: in September 1946, a Hospital Health Service was set up for all graduate nurses and Hospital employees.

Higher wages, a pension plan, and a larger staff were only a few items in the increased cost of operating the Kingston General Hospital. Once wartime controls were lifted there was a very sharp rise in prices. The wholesale price level rose thirty per cent in one year, 1947, to make the general level almost ninety per cent higher than before the war.

Drug prices skyrocketed. The basic supply stockpiled by the Hospital at the beginning of the war had not only run out of most drugs but had, in some cases, been superseded by new drugs. In six months in 1948, the Hospital spent $4,000 on streptomycin and the year's bill for penicillin reached $18,000. Superintendent Armstrong asked the Medical Staff to exercise care and to avoid waste in the use of these expensive drugs.

The use of antibiotics cut the length of a patient's stay in the Hospital but the preparation and administration of them required extra time and additional trained staff. Other new drugs, introduced before the war, such as heparin and dicumerol, which controlled clotting of the blood, were being used more often. Patients receiving those drugs had to be under the close care and constant supervision of specially trained personnel, since there were too many different situations for a standard procedure to be set up. The administration of these two drugs also made very frequent laboratory tests mandatory.

The laboratories, required to provide more tests and more elaborate procedures, operated at a loss. When the research division of the Richardson Laboratories discontinued various biological tests, the Hospital had to arrange for fuller biological service in the laboratories at the Hospital. The Queen's Laboratories servicing the Hospital did not do these tests under their contract and were not able to expand their service. Many tests were becoming more complicated. In the Biochemistry Laboratory, a serum phosphatase test required six working hours of the time of one technician. Some enzyme tests required about five hours. In the Metabolic Laboratory, tests were even more time-consuming and costly, some running through a week. The technicians who conducted these tests had to be more expert; they demanded commensurate salaries.

With the phenomenal growth of preventive medicine, the importance of diagnosis equalled, or even surpassed, that of treatment. Diagnostic services might amount to between thirty to seventy-five per cent of a patient's hospital bill. At the Kingston General Hospital, for instance, diagnostic X-ray work had increased twenty-one per cent in two years. The benefits to patients had increased proportionately. Gastric series made accurate diagnosis of stomach and bowel troubles more possible; bronchiograms revealed lung difficulties; and myelograms could reveal a protruding spinal disc so that bed rest or expert surgery could be prescribed.

Diagnosis was assisted also by new discoveries. On 16 November 1948, Dr. Burr reported to the Medical Staff that radio isotopes were available in Canada. Dr. Gleb Krotkov, a biologist at Queen's, had established a laboratory where some of the isotopes would be used in research and, said Dr. Burr, the Hospital should consider asking for isotopes to be used for medical purposes. A year later the Medical Conference Committee asked the Atomic Energy Commission of Canada if and when the Kingston General Hospital could introduce the use of radio-active iodine in tracer amounts.

The increased tempo of treatment was evident also in Surgery. New surgical procedures provided help for the patient throughout his stay in Hospital. All cases for operation were visited before and after the operation by the attending Anaesthetist. The number and complexity of operations made necessary more strict rules about scheduling operations, posting schedules and arranging for the assignment of the interns and special assistants. And no longer was a patient taken from the operating room directly to his own room. In the special Recovery Room he received constant supervision and extensive assisting therapy which had previously been used in only exceptional surgical cases. Blood, plasma, and oxygen therapy shortened the recovery time and hence allowed better use of the available Hospital beds.

By 1947 the total patient-day service at the Kingston General Hospital reached 143,472, compared to 81,766 fifteen years earlier. But the cost per patient-day had more than doubled. Each year service reached a new peak but so did expenses, and the revenue always fell a little behind. In 1948, for the first time in its history, the expenses and the revenue of the Kingston General Hospital both went over one million dollars. The deficit was $10,000.

It was the continuation of a problem which had always plagued the Hospital, as it did almost all other hospitals. Government grants never covered the complete cost of the 'free' patients. Private and semi-private patients had to be charged enough to meet losses in the public section. The out-patients, except for those attending some special clinics, were not supported by public grants. In 1949, the paying patients, either directly or through insurance, paid over seventy-five per cent of the cost of operating the Kingston General Hospital. The province and municipalities paid eighteen per cent, while donations, etc., brought in about six per cent.

The provincial operating grant had been increased and further increases were anticipated. The Municipal Statute Rate, however, was set at $3.00 a day per indigent patient, for a service that cost almost $7.00. And the City's very strict interpretation of indigency kept their payments down. Even the Ontario Hospital Insurance Plan was not meeting the demands of its members. In Kingston there had been a loss on the provincial plan since October 1944. Another loss was on the Queen's Student Health Plan, which was about to be renegotiated.

With operating expenses causing a deficit it was obviously impossible to expand accommodation without large, special, capital building funds. The Victory Progress Plan received fairly generous support from private donors, but implementation of the long-range plans had to depend on government support. The government capital grants system operated on a theoretical formula which worked to the disadvantage of the Kingston General Hospital. It was not just an area hospital which merited grants on the sole basis of the actual population in that specific area. It was a major teaching Hospital as well, serving a much wider public with more special services.

Planners in Kingston envisaged the Kingston General Hospital as a strong medical teaching Hospital, and a base Hospital for referrals from other community hospitals in all of eastern Ontario. Such a Hospital would be prepared to treat a high ratio of complicated cases, with adequate facilities and highly specialized staff. The Hospital planners were well aware that the achievement of their goal depended not only on provincial support for medical education but also on a close association of the Queen's Faculty of Medicine and the Kingston General Hospital.

As 1949 drew to a close, the larger building projects under immediate consideration were the Children's Hospital and the Walter T. Connell Wing. With other units to be erected later, the estimated cost was about three million dollars. The Governors were optimistic about achieving their goal while with practical good sense they authorized the erection of new buildings only as funds became available.

Nine

The decade of the 1950s in Canada is generally associated with peace and pros- *Government*
perity. But there were troubles both outside and inside the country which belied *Involvement*
that cliché. Canadian soldiers fought in the Korean war from 1950 to 1953. Brief *in Health*
recessions in 1953–1954 and 1957–1960 interrupted prosperity, but they had little *Care*
detrimental effect on the gross national product which doubled in the decade. *1950–1959*
There was practically no growth in agriculture. But the cities grew at an increasing rate with sprawling new suburbs, many of them made possible by Central
Mortgage and Housing Corporation loans.

Kingston, in 1952, annexed Portsmouth Village and a number of the suburbs
to increase its area by 5,585 acres and its population by 9,000. The total population
in the city was then 42,000 but before the end of the decade it had reached 50,000
with about 10,000 more in the new suburbs. There were some new industries in
and around the city but Kingston continued to be mainly an educational, military,
administrative, and service centre for eastern Ontario.

Social welfare programmes of the 1940s – the baby bonus and increased old age
pension payments – received, in the 1950s, more support from all levels of government. This support entailed more government control. The National Health
Grants Programme, passed in 1948, provided assistance to hospitals through medical schools and for approved hospital construction. It made grants also to some
special agencies, such as those combating cancer and tuberculosis. The most direct
grants were for the construction of patient accommodation. The federal and provincial governments participated in a joint programme to provide a certain amount
per new patient bed and per area of out-patient construction.

Those grants were indeed welcome. There was some apprehension, however, lest the hospitals receiving the grants lose some of their local autonomy and become part of a political machine. Two provinces had public, prepaid hospital care programmes by 1950. Ontario hospital administrators watched those operations with intense interest. The traditional policy of government grants was ideal for local administrative control but it failed to provide for a fair distribution of the cost burden.

The Governors of the Kingston General Hospital were concerned about this imbalance. Of the three partners giving them financial support, the patients contributed about seventy-five per cent, the greatest proportion. Furthermore, since government assistance for the indigent was inadequate, the private and semi-private patients helped to subsidize the care of the public patients. Many paying patients had hospital-care insurance which gave them substantial assistance and this insurance certainly eased the Hospital's concern about unpaid bills. But often the families without insurance could not afford to go into hospital.

Kingston General Hospital took advantage of government subsidies for the treatment of specific diseases, such as cancer, and for some special groups, such as veterans. Federal and provincial funds for new services and for research also supported certain types of work at the Hospital. Government assistance programmes grew piecemeal as needs arose and as new techniques and new treatments were developed. To take advantage of all the various programmes the Hospital had to have more space.

The Hospital also benefited from new voluntary societies, private groups interested in specific diseases. For example, the Canadian Arthritis and Rheumatism Society, organized in 1948, cooperated with professional and community groups. Their aim was to take practical measures to reduce the death and disability from rheumatic disease and their work was assisted by government grants as well as by voluntary contributions. In 1950, the Kingston General Hospital was one of four Ontario hospitals selected to establish Arthritis Clinics which were specifically to assist indigent out-patients. The Hospital was provided with the latest equipment for the treatment of arthritis and Dr. H. Garfield Kelly was put in charge of this new Clinic.

There was also help for the Hospital from other sources, The National Research Council helped to equip a Radio-active Isotope Laboratory in 1952. A J. P. Bickell Foundation grant in 1952 paid for the establishment of a Cardio-Vascular Laboratory to provide facilities for the investigation of patients with various forms of heart disease by certain specialized techniques, notably cardiac catheterization or by injection of radio-opaque substances into the vascular system. This laboratory was important because of the increasing possibilities of valvular surgery, especially in cases of mitral stenosis, and also because of advances in the management of congenital heart disease. An operating grant from the Ontario Heart Foundation supported the tests and research carried on here. But all of these grants for limited purposes did not provide the capital needed for major expansion.

The Board of Governors, with relief and some resentment, accepted the fact that capital grants for major Hospital buildings would be assured to their institution as a teaching Hospital associated with the Queen's University Faculty of Medicine. The traditional and complementary role of the Kingston General Hospital as a community Hospital seemed to be quite subordinate. Appeals to the Ontario government had met with no success until the Board emphasized the special needs of a teaching Hospital. They received an immediate grant, through Queen's, of $275,000. The Hospital was able, with that support, to begin the implementation of a plan to expand and modernize the Hospital during the 1950s.

One of the first needs in modernizing the Hospital was to bring the heating system up to standards of safety and comfort, with economic efficiency. By 1952, sixty per cent of the heating system was improved without any major disruption of service. Another problem was the electric power situation together with the provision of storage and workshop space. Renovations, with their temporary moves, sudden though minor disruptions of service, and workmen under foot, put a strain on facilities and on personnel. Nor was it easy to find the funds for such work. The province finally recognized the problem and, in 1953, made a special rehabilitation grant to the Hospital of $165,000. The money was to be used not for current maintenance but to replace some obsolete equipment and to renovate old areas such as the Doran Wing.

At that time, Dr. R. R. MacGregor, Chief of Paediatrics, looked forward to leaving the Doran Wing, which had seemed so excellent twenty years before. The plans for a special Children's Hospital had been initiated in 1938, when the Board decided that such a project would be a way to celebrate the centenary of the Hospital in 1945. But the war intervened. When plans for future expansion were being considered just before the end of the war, the Kingston Shrine Club offered to start a fund for a special unit for children. The 1945 Hospital campaign for funds was specifically for the extension to the Empire Wing. Consequently, when a volunteer committee decided to raise funds for a children's hospital they set up a separate organization. They decided to conduct each year at Christmas time a continuing campaign for money to add to the available government grant. The Kingston Shrine Club pledged themselves to a major contribution to the fund and to continuing support. With this commitment the Shriners were asked to suggest a name for the hospital. The name chosen was Angada, an Arabic word meaning 'to bring help to you.' Dr. John Tweddell was the first Chairman of the Angada Hospital Committee.

Contracts for Angada were let in December 1950. Construction disrupted the operation of the Paediatrics Department. Child patients were scattered about the

Hospital wherever beds were available. That was a return to the situation as it had been before 1892 when the St. Andrews Children's Ward was opened in the attic of the Watkins Wing.

Angada was completed in 1953 and opened officially by Lieutenant Governor Braithwaite. It was the only children's hospital between Toronto and Montreal. The four floors provided eighty-two beds and treatment centres for infants, pre-schoolers, school age children, and high school students. Clinical Laboratories were moved into Angada to occupy the basement. Doran was then reconstructed to accommodate various other services.

The two projects yet to be accomplished in the Victory Progress Plan were a new Dietary Wing and a major extension behind the Douglas Wing, to be called the Walter T. Connell Wing. Estimates for those buildings had reached about $3,000,000 and the Building Fund, though handsomely supported by doctors and administrators, grew slowly. Construction could not be started until more money was available and a sum of that size had to come mostly from the government. A certain delay was inevitable. Though the Victory Progress Plan was constantly re-considered to meet immediate needs and new medical advances, its basic aim remained unchanged: the Kingston General Hospital should be developed as a medical centre where a wide variety of treatments would be available. It would be a regional general hospital as well as a major teaching hospital. There would be an emphasis on highly specialized treatment for complicated cases, necessarily requir-ing costly facilities and highly trained specialists not otherwise available in the area. Such a plan imposed special demands on space and on financing. The financing would depend mainly on government.

The 1952 report of the Ontario Health Survey Committee was, consequently, especially disturbing to both the Hospital and the Queen's Faculty of Medicine. The Committee had considered the province by regions. Region number four in-cluded the counties of Hastings, Lennox and Addington, Leeds and Grenville, and Frontenac. Kingston was the medical centre of the region. The report, finding in this region a high ratio of beds per thousand residents, recommended a very small bed increase in 1953 and none in 1954.

The Governors could not reconcile such a finding with the long waiting list of applicants for admission to Kingston General Hospital. The list often reached three hundred. A bed occupancy rate approaching ninety per cent made it very difficult to provide proper accommodation for emergency admissions. In addition, it was not easy for Housekeeping to clean, paint, and maintain the rooms and services in the most desirable manner. There seemed, to the Governors of the Hospital, to be only one solution to the problem – more beds.

One chart in the Committee report supported the Governors' contention. It showed that the number of days of hospital service for this region was second to only one other region in the province. It was evident that some readjustment of figures was necessary. The idea of an expanding medical centre should not be threatened by statistics. Superintendent Armstrong suggested that the Hospital was drawing from an area of 400,000 persons rather than the 219,000 estimated in the report.

The Hospital and Queen's decided to join forces to present a united appeal to the government. In 1953, they set up a Joint Planning Committee with the Dean of Medicine, Dr. G. H. Ettinger, as Chairman. However, the increased government support, beginning in 1954, made the situation less critical and the Joint Committee was only moderately active.

The Hospital as a medical centre was already a reality. The distinguished staff of specialists attracted unusual problem cases, especially in surgery. Also, as a university teaching Hospital it attracted interesting and unusual clinical cases. The Cancer Clinic was the first official regional service at the Hospital. The original ten-year grant for the Clinic was established on a permanent basis to provide funds through the Ontario Cancer Foundation for this regional clinic.

In 1952, Superintendent Fraser Armstrong talking to the Kiwanis Club, discussed a regional hospital scheme, one that would emphasize voluntary coordination rather than competition. He mentioned, in particular, that such regional planning would be especially valuable in laboratories, some of which were even then operating on an unofficial regional basis. Laboratory work for the region was divided among the local Ontario Department of Health Laboratory, Queen's, and the Hospital. At that time the only pathologists in eastern Ontario were in Ottawa, Peterborough, and Kingston. All of the biopsies and haematological specimens were sent to the Queen's–Hospital laboratories for examination. Kingston was the ideal centre for an official regional service.

The Clinical Laboratories at the Hospital had been enlarged to cope with the extension of services and new staff was hired. Dr. G. F. Kipkie (Queen's and McGill) came from Duke University to become Director of the Clinical Laboratories and Associate Professor of Pathology at Queen's. Dr. John Hamilton resigned in 1951 and Dr. R. H. More succeeded him as Head of the Department of Pathology. For years the Pathology Department was responsible for the whole laboratory operation. In the early 1950s Dr. More and Dr. Kipkie developed laboratory sub-departments and put them in charge of specialists who were not pathologists. It was very advanced thinking for that time.

Dr. D. L. Wilson (Queen's 1944) had joined the Department of Medicine in 1951. When the Laboratories were moved into the basement of the new Angada building in 1953, he supervised the Biochemistry Laboratory as a part-time job. Dr. N. A. Hinton (Queen's 1951) was appointed to cope with the increased work in the Bacteriology Laboratory. Dr. H. D. Steele (Queen's 1944) joined the department in 1953 and became Associate Director of the Laboratories and Director of the Blood Bank in 1957. Dr. W. D. Hay (Queen's 1921) retired that year after long service as an Associate in the Department. The laboratory work continued to grow as new tests were devised and as research and teaching programmes were further emphasized.

When the Angada Wing was in full operation and running smoothly, Dr. Rob Roy MacGregor retired as Director of Paediatrics. Dr. Alex M. Bryans, of Toronto, became head of the section in 1956. Another long time staff member in that department, Dr. John Delahaye (Queen's 1927), also retired. His son, Dr. Donald Delahaye (Queen's 1950), who had joined the department in 1954, assisted Dr. Bryans. They developed over the next few years a special centre for the clinical management of haemolytic diseases of the new-born, involving replacement transfusions. The Hospital was the centre for special medical care of all children as Angada served a wide area in this part of the province.

There were other staff changes through retirement and the expansion of services. Dr. Frederick Cays, who had first served under Dr. J. C. Connell in 1912, retired in 1954. Dr. David Rosen (McGill) with extensive training in Ophthalmology came to be head of that department at the Hospital and at the University. Dr. G. B. Macpherson was made head of a new Department of Otorhinolaryngology. Dr. James Purvis (Queen's 1952) and Dr. J. G. McBroom (Queen's 1934) were associated with him and with Dr. Rosen.

The expansion and specialization of staff was also evident in Surgery. The Department of Surgery doubled in five years. The great strides made in thoracic, orthopaedic, and abdominal surgery required specialists and a medical centre to which referrals could be made in difficult cases. The Hospital and Queen's attracted the specialists. In 1954 there were five doctors in the department. In 1955 the Senior Surgeons were Doctors Bingham, Boucher, and Houston; the Assistant Attending Surgeons were Doctors W. R. Ghent (Queen's 1947) and H. M. Warner (McGill). Dr. Ross Tilley continued as Consulting Plastic Surgeon. Dr. W. J. S. Melvin (Queen's 1943), son of Dr. G. S. Melvin, was listed as the Orthopaedic Surgeon, with Dr. J. W. Hazlett (Toronto) as an assistant in that specialty. In 1958 two more appointments gave added strength to the department and offered new services in Surgery. Dr. R. F. Hetherington (Toronto and Oxford) was a Neurosurgeon. Dr. Beverly Lynn (Queen's 1945) did specialist study in Edinburgh and came to the Hospital to take charge of the Cardio-Vascular Division in Surgery. All of these appointments were for part-time work, for while the surgeons were consultants and teachers they also had private practices.

In the Department of Medicine Dr. Ford Connell carried on a programme of expansion which revolutionized the medical school and the clinical teaching at the Hospital. Over a period of years he brought one doctor after another into the department as full-time staff, progressive, energetic men who developed further their own specialties, men such as Doctors D. L. Wilson, H. G. Kelly, and Malcolm Brown, who were constantly available to the great benefit of patients and interns.

As specialties were developed and new approaches to health problems were made, new services were inaugurated and existing ones expanded. Dr. Ford Connell continued to pursue his own work in the Cardiology Department and organized some subdivisions to attract specialists and to take advantage of available grants. In 1956, Dr. Connell and Dr. George Mayer (Budapest and Queen's) set up an Anticoagulant Service to aid in the management of patients requiring short or long term anticoagulant treatment for coronary thrombosis, thrombophlebitis, pulmonary infarction, and similar disorders. The service grew out of research carried on by the two doctors under a J. P. Bickell Foundation grant. In 1958 they received a Schering Corporation grant to assist them. They developed a standard clotting time as a research tool but were soon using it clinically to control heparin dosage and to screen patients for abnormal bleeding tendencies. The service was so much in demand, with emergency calls at all hours, that a staff of only four had problems coping with the work. This Anticoagulant Service was then unique in Canada and was, by 1959, the third largest hospital anticoagulant service in the world.

Grants from the Richardson Fund at Queen's, the Bickell Foundation and the Ontario Heart Foundation made possible the development of another special service. A Cardio-Pulmonary Laboratory was established in 1956 with Dr. H. G. Kelly in charge, assisted by Dr. J. D. Hatcher (Western). It was equipped to carry out pulmonary function tests needed in the diagnostic service, and to make possible some further research projects.

Nurses as well as doctors developed specialties. The nursing section set up an Intravenous Therapy Service in January 1955, to handle the greatly increased use of this specialty in both diagnosis and treatment. A specially trained team of a Supervisor and two graduate nurses was in charge of beginning all intravenous infusions, taking blood for tests and starting blood transfusions. They worked from 7 a.m. to 7 p.m., after which an intern took over their duties. This marked a change in the regulations which had required a doctor to be in charge of such duties. It also indicated a trend to give more para-medical responsibilities to specially trained graduate nurses.

Some departments which had existed with minimal, or even just part-time, help were given new status and new staff. Psychiatry had been a department with Dr. C. H. McCuaig, of the Ontario Psychiatric Hospital, giving part-time to its direction. In 1957 Dr. R. Bruce Sloan came to give full-time to that work. The next year the staff was increased by the appointments of Dr. George Laverty, Psychiatrist, and Dr. J. Inglis, Psychologist, both trained in Edinburgh and London. They worked toward a unification of the psychiatric services in the Hospital and instituted out-patient services.

Specialization within the department occurred also in other departments. In Diagnostic Radiology Dr. W. A. Jones's staff grew steadily in cramped quarters to cope with a large work load. Dr. Colwell, the Neuro-radiologist, joined the staff at Hotel Dieu, but continued to give part-time service to the Kingston General Hospital. At the end of 1955, Dr. S. L. Fransman, trained in Amsterdam, was appointed as a specialist in Thoracic Radiology. A Paediatric Radiologist joined the department in 1957. By the end of the decade Radiology had six doctors on staff and three graduate physicians in training to handle the patient load which had increased by almost 5,000 patients a year in less than five years.

All Therapeutic Radiology was done under the direction of Dr. R .C. Burr in the Cancer Clinic. Dr. A. F. Holloway, a Radiation Physicist, was appointed in 1956 to take charge of the Clinic laboratory and the instrument shop. The Cancer Clinic gained additional space when a section was built on the ground floor of the Victory Wing to house cobalt beam therapy. The case load continued to increase and Dr. Frank Batley, a Radio Therapist, joined the staff. He was succeeded in 1959, by Dr. James Frame of Edinburgh. When the medical offices were moved to the new Etherington Hall, the Cancer Clinic expanded into the free space on the ground floor of the Victory Wing.

There was, in some fields, a consolidation of related services under one department. The Department of Rehabilitation Medicine, in 1956, was directed by Dr. H. G. Kelly as a part-time job. Included in the department were Physiotherapy, Occupational Therapy, and the Medical Social Service, each with a Director. The last division had been inaugurated in 1953, with Miss Constance Fraser in charge, to give assistance to the aged and chronically ill patients who were ready to leave Hospital. Their release was often delayed because of a lack of proper facilities for their care elsewhere in the city. Miss Fraser's report, in 1954, indicated the need for a city rehabilitation centre and a family agency or homemakers' service. The opening of new wings at St. Mary's of the Lake Hospital and at Rideaucrest Home for the Aged in 1955, eased the most immediate placement problems. But there were seldom case workers enough to handle all the referrals.

There was some consolidation also in the supporting services at the Hospital. A Central Surgical Supply was established in 1952. It brought together under one responsible head, the cleansing, sterilizing, servicing, and preparation of material used in major treatments and in many diagnostic tests. However, complete physical centralization of such supplies and equipment was impossible until space in the new W. T. Connell Wing became available. When Miss Margaret Blair retired in 1957 as Supervisor of the Operating Room, she was made head of this service.

Construction of the Connell Wing began in 1956 and as funds became available, succeeding contracts for further construction of the Wing were let. The contract for completion of the building was signed in 1958. Long before it was completed, however, the need for more space was particularly acute. Pharmacy, for instance, was occupying the space it had when the Hospital was half the size. And all departments and supporting services continued to grow.

The work and problems of administration also increased. The Chairmen of the Board of Governors in the 1950s were: A. L. Davies, David Rankin, Dr. Stuart Polson, R. C. Oaks, and A. N. Chown. In the Management Committee they faced and dealt with the problems of an increasing tempo of change and growth. The extent of some of those problems is shown very clearly in financial reports. In 1955, the Hospital expenditure was over two million dollars, a hundred per cent increase since 1948. Three years later the expenditure had reached almost three million. Fortunately the income had risen correspondingly but there was, as usual, a small deficit.

For that expenditure the Hospital provided almost 150,000 days of patient care, an increase of 50,000 days in ten years. What statistics could not show was the increase in the quality of patient care. The Governors were justly proud of the fact that the highest service standards had been maintained or raised while, for a period of thirty years, revenue and expense had been kept in balance.

Change was evident in the Board of Governors which marked, in this decade, the death of former Chairmen Manly Baker, E. W. Waldron, Elmer Davis, and David Rankin. They noted with regret the deaths of former Queen's University administrators: Principal R. C. Wallace, Vice-Principal W. E. McNeill and Dean of Applied Science A. L. Clark, who had also served on the Board. The Board's solicitor, J. M. Farrell, and their historian, Edwin Horsey, died in the 1950s.

Dr. Frederick Etherington and Dr. G. W. Mylks, Sr., former chiefs of Hospital departments, died after having been retired for some time. Two employees of long standing were also mourned. Miss Emma Sharpe, a 1930 graduate of the School of Nursing, died in 1952. She served as a Supervisor for twenty years, first of Douglas then of Out-patients. In 1958, Miss Emma Hunter, devoted and beloved employee, died. She had joined the Hospital staff in 1899 as their first stenographer, and, in spite of recent ill health, continued with some lighter duties until her final illness.

The Governors, in 1956, under Chairman Stuart Polson, faced major personnel problems. Superintendent Fraser Armstrong informed the Board that he wished to retire as soon as a suitable replacement could be found. Assistant Superintendent, Miss Olevia Wilson, and Director of Nursing, Miss Louise Acton, also announced that they wished to retire as soon as convenient. That was a blow to the Board; the replacement of three top administrators was a formidable task. Those three people had each been in key positions at the Kingston General Hospital for over thirty years.

Fraser Armstrong administered the Hospital for the Committee of Management for thirty-one years, with diplomacy, skill, and financial success. His high standing in the field of hospital administration was well-known. In March 1957, he received the George Finlay Stevens Memorial Award, given by the Canadian Hospital Association for distinguished contribution to the hospital field.

The Board made a long and careful search for a highly qualified man to be the new superintendent. Donald M. MacIntyre was appointed in 1957 to take over his duties on 1 January 1958. Mr. MacIntyre, a native of Ontario, grew up in Saskatchewan and graduated from university there. After further studies he received diplomas in Public and in Hospital Administration. He had extensive experience in hospital work, and in government, teaching, and administrative positions. Mr. MacIntyre came to Kingston from Kitimat, B.C., where he had been hospital administrator for the Aluminum Company of Canada.

The new Superintendent took over the administration of the Kingston General Hospital at a critical point in its history. After over a century of independent operation it had to adjust to careful budgeting under government supervision. It was not, strictly speaking, a university hospital, yet it had a traditional and very close connection with the Queen's University Faculty of Medicine. As part of a teaching medical centre it was able to attract well-qualified, professional personnel and a good house staff. Such a centre also required an adequate supply of clinical material, as the Hospital's continued expansion depended on its role and quality as a teaching hospital. It was also a regional hospital and had strong ties with the immediate community. With 513 beds, it was the largest as well as the best equipped hospital in the area.

The Hospital was in the final stages of a building programme and new plans for the future were needed if ordered expansion was to continue. The replacement of three executives at once would cause serious disruption in administration. Fraser Armstrong agreed to stay on as consultant on the Connell Wing and to see to the planning and contracting for the Dietary Wing, the final projects in the Victory Progress Plan. The new Superintendent could look to the future after he settled into his job. Miss Wilson continued to act as Assistant Superintendent in order to facilitate the changeover of administrators.

In 1958, there were a great number of changes in the nursing staff, departures and transfers within the Hospital. In July, Miss Hazel Miller came from the nursing science course at McGill to replace Miss Louise Acton as Director of Nursing. The appointment of a Director of Nursing Education, Miss Jean Goddard, to work for Miss Miller, was the first step towards the separation of the teaching department from the nursing staff. Some full-time teaching appointments were made in the Training School and the clinical teaching staff was increased. Students enrolled in the School of Nursing in 1958 numbered 197. The nursing staff at the Hospital included 140 registered nurses, three non-registered, four certified nursing assistants, and 70 ward aides. Miss Hilda Lake became Director of Nursing Education following Miss Goddard's resignation in 1959.

The Victory Progress Plan would be complete when the Walter T. Connell Wing and the Dietary Wing were finished. The total cost of the Plan was almost six million dollars. Yet there was still a need for more space and for anticipated expansion. The Board of Governors decided to seek professional advice so that they could set up another long range plan. They hired, in 1958, the firm of Agnew, Peckham and Associates, Hospital Consultants, to prepare recommendations for the next ten to twenty years.

The plan would have to show, among other things, how the Hospital could develop under the new government legislation. In January 1956, the federal government offered grants in aid to assist in the establishment of nationwide hospital insurance. The federal grants had to be matched by provincial grants and to be administered by the province. Five provinces, including Ontario, joined the scheme by July 1958. So the national programme began on 1 July 1958; the Ontario programme on 1 January 1959. Administration in Ontario was by the Ontario Hospital Services Commission.

A number of the Kingston General Hospital departments expected that this new government hospital programme would tax their resources. With the accent on diagnostic services even the planned expansion of the Hospital into the Connell Wing would be inadequate. There was some apprehension, too, about the effect of the Act on the operation of the Hospital. How much control would government assume over the Hospital and the patients? There was a good deal of misunderstanding by the general public about the Act.

At a meeting of the Board of Governors in March 1959, Chairman R. C. Oaks told the members that, in accordance with the government hospital scheme, the Ontario Hospital Services Commission had issued a directive to the Hospital regarding the schedule of fees that could be charged for its services. Detailed records would have to be kept for a government audit. The internal management of the Hospital, he said, would continue as usual, under the direction of the Board. That statement, to the administrators of the Hospital who were struggling with the required figures, statistics, and reports for the government, may have seemed to be an oversimplification.

Superintendent MacIntyre in his very first year on the job, had to do more than merely take over the administration of the Hospital. He had to gear the organization to work, in accord not only with the provisions of the Ontario Hospital Act but also with the procedures prescribed by the Ontario Hospital Services Commission. The statistical and accounting records were brought into line with the requirements of the Commission. The greatest change was in the budget system of operation. Each department had to submit a detailed budget and keep its expenditures within the approved amount. The reconstituted Medical Conference and Advisory Committee at Kingston General Hospital was of great value in reorganizing the administrative procedures.

Under the new scheme the income from patient care, paid by the government insurance, met ninety-four per cent of the cost of the operation of the Hospital. The government continued also to make capital building grants and provided $668,023.40 to complete the construction already under way at the Kingston General Hospital. Any future capital grants would become available only if the Hospital itself produced some supplementary funds.

Another major change was in the operation of the Blood Bank under the Ontario Hospital Services Commission. The Red Cross was designated as the agency to collect and to supply blood to all Ontario hospitals. The supply depot for Kingston was in Ottawa, with shipments to Kingston twice a week and on demand in emergencies. Pressure on space for the Blood Bank at the Hospital was thus temporarily relieved. And the problem of getting a sufficient number of donors was passed on to the Red Cross.

The Clinical Laboratories were immediately affected by the operation of the Hospital Act; they experienced a great increase in their work load. The growing emphasis on diagnostic work was evident not only in the Laboratories but also in Radiology. That department reported that the total number of examinations had risen from 12,536 in 1954 to 18,710 in 1959. What added greatly to their work load was the increasing complexity of certain examinations and the calls on the professional staff for interdepartmental activities and consultations.

Many of the Hospital services had hired extra staff in anticipation of an increased patient load. Those services, consequently, suffered only from lack of space. Even the problem of space was temporarily eased in some areas. The Isolation Hospital had, for some time, not been used by more than a very few patients because of the decline in the incidence of communicable diseases. The City of Kingston agreed to sell it for one dollar to the General Hospital, which had always been responsible for its operation. The ground floor was reserved for the City Department of Health. The other floors were renovated to accommodate twenty-seven beds for long-term patients with chronic disabilities or degenerative diseases.

Early in 1959, Etherington Hall, a new Queen's building, was opened. Built beside the Richardson Laboratories and connected to them, it provided facilities for expanded diagnostic service and for additional research. There was space for teaching and for offices for the heads of the medical departments at the Hospital. Those were the men who tied the Hospital and the Queen's Medical Faculty so closely together that the dividing line was not at all clear. They were appointed by Queen's as the heads of their respective departments in the Faculty of Medicine. They were also appointed by the Board of Governors of the Hospital to be chiefs of their respective services at the Hospital. However, the Hospital appointments, according to the Medical Staff by-laws, were made only upon recommendation by the Trustees of Queen's University.

That the two appointments – as head of a University department and chief of a Hospital service – should be linked together was logical. The clinical teaching staff at the Hospital had also to be acceptable to the University. But, since the by-laws did not specifically provide for Hospital approval of the appointments, the Board felt that it was often called upon to be merely a rubber stamp. It was only in a very few instances that appointments to the clinical staff, not chiefs of services, had been made without prior consultation with the Hospital administration. But those few instances had caused ill feeling; obviously, the relationship and the communication between the two institutions needed to be improved.

In 1958 a Joint Queen's–Hospital Committee, which had been set up in 1953, was reactivated to assist in working out relationships in areas of common interest. This committee was composed of the Chairman of the Board and the Superintendent of the Hospital, and the Principal and the Dean of Medicine of Queen's. Deliberations, very informal at first, soon became more formal as the committee's recommendations affected both partners at a critical time in their development. The committee was concerned both with presentations to the government and with the actions of two internal committees.

Those internal committees represented the different viewpoints of the two partners. The University Medical Advisory Committee advised the Dean of Medicine respecting matters pertaining to the Faculty of Medicine, including those of teaching at the Hospital. Their recommendations were made from the viewpoint of medical education rather than from that of patient care. The Medical Conference Advisory Committee at the Hospital advised the Superintendent and the Management Committee on professional matters at the Hospital. Those matters concerned both patient care and medical education, from the viewpoint of the Hospital. And decisions on admitting privileges, non-teaching staff appointments, and reserved beds affected not only the University and the Hospital but also all doctors in the area.

Even more difficult than a division of responsibilities was a division of the costs between the two partners. To apportion the doctors' time, salary, supplies, research assistants, and special funds in a definite budget, as required by the government, needed specialized cost accounting. It was sometimes found, as in the case of the Cardio-Pulmonary Laboratory, to be best for Queen's to pay the full cost and to sell the Laboratory services to the Hospital.

It became evident by the end of the decade that there should be a senior administrator who could devote full-time to the professional medical side of the Hospital. He would provide liaison between the Superintendent and the Medical Staff. Dr. D. L. Wilson, as a member of both the Intern Committee and the Medical Conference Advisory Committee, had carried out these duties in addition to his clinical and laboratory work. Management decided to look for a doctor, not in practice and not in the Kingston area, who could do the job. He would be not only the consultative link for immediate communication between administration and the professional staff, but also a neutral but informed voice in possible conflicts of interest. Management was not able, at the time, to find such a doctor. But the Committee made an appointment since they felt that it was necessary to relieve the Superintendent of this direct responsibility. Mr. Peter Carruthers from the Winnipeg General Hospital joined the staff as Assistant Superintendent (Professional).

More administrative changes were necessary at the Hospital as its operation became more complex. Paperwork increased under the new government regulations. The reduction of the work week to forty hours made necessary a bigger supporting staff. Early in 1959, Mr. Slade Nix was appointed to be the first full-time personnel director assisted by Mrs. Margaret Thom, taking over duties that had formerly been parcelled out to various departments. He dealt first with comprehensive salary reviews and a new pension plan for employees.

In 1958, Dr. Bruce Young (Queen's 1940) came from Toronto to become head of the Rehabilitation Department. The next year the department was selected as a training facility for the new School of Occupational Therapy that had just opened on the Queen's campus. Consequently, there followed some staff changes and an increased teaching load. But there was also some hope that the serious shortage of trained therapists might be eased. In the same department the Medical Social Service had more cases than they could handle. The new hospital insurance plan created a tendency among old people to seek custodial care in a hospital. That was an intensification of the problem the Hospital had had throughout its history.

In many departments there were new methods of treatment, more work, and some staff changes. Dr. W. A. Campbell, Chief of the Department of Anaesthesiology, asked to be relieved of the administrative work, pending retirement. Dr. Stuart L. Vandewater, who received his medical degree at Toronto, became the chief of the department.

The Board of Governors still had financial problems. The main operating costs of the Hospital were met by government funds under the Hospital Act. But no capital grants were made for new equipment. Half of the cost of approved new construction and two-thirds of the costs of approved renovations were provided for in the government capital grant structure. But the other half or one-third had to come from the community whose continued support was necessary.

Volunteer groups continued to make donations of equipment, money and time to the Hospital. The Kingston Medical Wives' Society presented two index wheels to the Poison Control Centre in the Out-patients' Department. These wheels provided, on cards supplied by the government, immediate information on poisons and their antidotes. It was another service provided by the Hospital which had not before been so conveniently available in Kingston. The Women's Aid volunteer group had continued to grow. In 1958, with almost two hundred and fifty volunteers, a centralized administration was necessary. A part-time Director, Mrs. Doris Brebner, was paid by the Women's Aid to take charge of the many volunteer workers at the Hospital. That same year, the Women's Aid agreed to pay the salary of the first Play Therapist to work in the Paediatrics Department.

The Kingston General Hospital completed its first year of operation under the new Ontario Hospital Services Commission, with no special problems. The main adjustments had been made; the results would appear in future operations.

Ten

The successful launching of the government hospital insurance scheme brought *Progress* major developments in health care in the 1960s. With hospital care available to all, *towards a* it soon became evident that existing facilities and personnel were insufficient to *Health* serve the number of people who needed that care. It also became clear that many *Sciences* people were being put into hospital who did not need bed care. But the government *Centre* paid for medical services only in the hospitals. The intense pressure on hospital *1960–1972* accommodation could be eased only if provision were made for insured medical services performed outside of the hospitals.

For some years many people had benefited by medical insurance plans operated by private companies, mainly through group insurance. This did not, however, meet the needs of a large portion of the public who did not, or could not, belong to such plans. To meet their needs in health care and in housing, both the federal and provincial governments were moving into more social assistance programmes.

Problems of the poor and the elderly were particularly acute. The effect of improved medical knowledge and treatment was evident in the increasing number of older citizens. And the changed mode of family life left many of these old people in need of public assistance in both housing and health care. Furthermore, emphasis on preventive medicine made it important that all citizens, young and old, should have access to the health care they could afford.

By the middle of the decade, Ontario had enacted a Medical Services Insurance Plan to make health care available to all citizens. The cost was small for those who could afford to pay; others were given free care. OMSIP, as it became known, took effect 1 April 1966. This plan further accentuated the demand for doctors, nurses, and other associated personnel to deliver the health care. Consequently, additional stress was put on training facilities, not only for doctors and nurses but also for special personnel in many supporting services.

A survey of medical training facilities in 1963 noted the needs at that time and brought to light additional requirements in the field of medical research. As a result, to consolidate these demands, a new order of health-related activities had been created even before OMSIP was instituted.

The increasing demand on hospitals, as centres of patient care, teaching, and clinical research, was most evident in the teaching hospitals affiliated with universities and medical schools. The Kingston General Hospital was one of the four major teaching hospitals in Ontario affiliated with a medical school. Furthermore, it had a School of Nursing and smaller auxiliary programmes for the training of X-ray technologists and laboratory technicians. Classes for operating room technicians and for certified nursing assistants were being organized at the Hospital. And students of hospital administration, social work, and occupational and physical therapy did practice work in the Hospital. As one of the larger hospitals in the province, and as a general hospital equipped to diagnose and treat a wide variety of illnesses and injuries, it was more and more impelled to expand in patient service and accommodation.

The Kingston General Hospital celebrated the completion of its Victory Progress Plan in 1960. Although the planning for a major expansion had been started in 1940, the first major addition under that plan had been the Victory Wing, completed in 1947. The last buildings erected under the Victory Progress Plan were the Dietary Wing and the Walter T. Connell Wing, opened in 1960.

The Dietary unit, a three storey building between the Victory Wing and the new Connell Wing, was in full operation by the first of July. Dietitian Beth Nelson planned the unit and the system but left to be married before it was in operation. Former Superintendent Armstrong supervised the completion of the unit. The up-to-date and greatly enlarged dietary operation replaced an obsolete and decentralized system which had been expanded piecemeal for almost twenty years. The new unit handled the cooking and preparation of food for about 1,400 meals a day. All meals were prepared and trays made up in the main kitchen and delivered in special carts to the wards. The third floor of the unit was a staff cafeteria seating 350 persons.

The Walter T. Connell Wing was officially opened in June 1960. A seven storey building 256 feet long and 72 feet wide, it was designed to provide 128 beds for patients. But perhaps of more importance was the number of new and enlarged service departments housed in what was at the time an ultra-modern building. New accommodations for the Emergency Department, for Out-patients, Clinics, Medical Records, and Pharmacy were well equipped and many times the size of their previous quarters.

The second floor was devoted to operating rooms, recovery rooms, and related areas, all air-conditioned and furnished with the most up-to-date equipment. Of the ten new operating theatres five were for general surgery. The others were designed for a number of specialties: urology, orthopaedic, fractures, neuro-surgery, and cardiac surgery.

The third floor provided forty-six beds for medical patients. The fourth floor had beds and treatment facilities for psychiatric patients. This was the first carefully planned provision for the treatment of emotionally disturbed patients as an integral part of the Kingston General Hospital. The highly trained staff and the special treatment provided were in accord with the latest approach to mental disease.

The top three floors of the Connell Wing housed a new and much enlarged Maternity Department. The floor plan was the result of careful study, by the staff in the department and the architect, of the best arrangements to meet high hospital standards and teaching requirements. Dr. Edwin Robertson, Chief of Obstetrics and Gynaecology, brought in a concept very different from that of the traditional maternity department. He insisted that the teaching facilities form an integral part of the whole design of that section.

The generous space and modern equipment in all the departments housed in the new wing benefited the patients and the staff, and enriched the opportunities for teaching. The Connell Wing was also designed and constructed so that additional floors could be added later.

With the opening of the Connell Wing it was possible to release some of the older sections of the Hospital for renovations and other uses. When the Maternity Department moved from its cramped quarters in the Nickle Wing, that space was renovated. It became a Selective Care Unit for ambulatory patients who could, to some degree, care for themselves. This minimal care section took pressure off the active treatment wards and allowed a more efficient use of the nurses assigned to Nickle. The top floor of this Wing was used by the School for X-ray Technicians.

The Douglas Wing also was extensively renovated to provide by 1962 more modern facilities for medical and surgical patients. It had an Intensive Care Unit with all necessary services for cases requiring constant supervision. All of the first floor was used by the Department of Radiology, giving more adequate space for the diagnostic use of X-ray. The fourth and fifth floors contained the Clinical Laboratories and the Blood Bank. These Hospital laboratory facilities were then integrated with those of Queen's University in the adjacent Richardson Building. This instance of cooperative planning avoided some unnecessary duplication and achieved a laboratory larger and better equipped to the benefit of both partners and of the patients.

The trend toward the incorporation of isolation facilities into the various nursing units in the Hospital had caused the Isolation Hospital to become obsolete as a separate unit. A generous gift from the estate of George Bawden made the renovation of that building possible. It was set up as a rehabilitation centre for convalescent patients – those with cardiac, arthritic, orthopaedic, or neurological conditions who could benefit from a combination of treatment and training. When the renovations were all completed, in 1962, the Kingston General Hospital had an in-patient capacity of 598 beds and 71 bassinets. The out-patient and clinical facilities were also greatly increased.

Those renovations and relocations of services were part of the new plan for the Hospital contained in the Agnew Report. The Agnew firm of hospital consultants, commissioned in 1958 to prepare a long range plan for the Hospital, submitted its report in August 1960. They had been directed to make a study of the Hospital facilities, patient services, administration, and relationship with the University and with the community. In the light of those terms of reference the firm submitted recommendations for the development and expansion of accommodation and services and for the general administration of the Kingston General Hospital.

The Agnew Report listed fifty-six recommendations under seven headings. They were not all for changes; a number of departments were found to be quite satisfactory with the completion of the Connell Wing. A limit of 800 beds as the ultimate goal, with 750 provided by 1970, was set as the desired capacity of the Hospital. The Report's strongest and most urgent recommendations concerned improved facilities for laundry, housekeeping, and central storage. It also advised the immediate provision of employee facilities and of parking for doctors, visitors, and employees.

Under the heading Educational and Residential Facilities, the Report made eight recommendations for improvement. They had to do with the provision of proper residences for interns and for nurses and an education building for the School of Nursing. The Report also recommended the further development of the teaching of technicians and of an expanded programme for postgraduate medical education.

Other recommendations in the Agnew Report concerned Hospital-University relations, staff, and administrative organization. The need for more consultation and better communication between Queen's and the Hospital was emphasized. Administrative reorganization at the Hospital was recommended in order to consolidate duties and to relieve the Superintendent of matters of detail.

The long range building programme dealt with recommendations for the progressive demolition of old buildings and the proper site development for new ones. It was difficult to find an economically sound plan which would permit continued and proper operation of the Hospital during extensive renovations and new construction. Furthermore, plans for large capital expenditures were dependent on the approval of the provincial and federal governments.

The Kingston General Hospital planning for the future was in tune with the changing times. Yet the tempo of change increased and the plans had to be continually adjusted. The Board of Governors, chaired in 1961 by Bruce Matthews, knew that future plans for the Hospital had to be geared to national and provincial policies, as well as being concerned with the best interests of the community and of the Hospital. These considerations caused a certain delay in effecting all of the building recommendations contained in the Agnew Report.

Meanwhile the Hospital continued to provide health care, teaching and research facilities although major physical expansion was delayed. The exterior appearance of the Hospital underwent little change in the first half of the decade but there were significant interior changes and a further development of services.

Major adjustments had already been made in the business office to deal with the requirements of the Ontario Hospital Services Commission. Bernard Tetro became Comptroller and E. H. Mills took charge of the Purchasing Department. With a total expenditure for 1960 of over $4,000,000 in a plant valued at over $9,000,000 Kingston General Hospital had become big business.

The reorganization of the administration gave Superintendent D. M. MacIntyre a number of senior assistants with new titles. William Robb was appointed Assistant Administrator (Plant); Peter Carruthers, Assistant Administrator (Professional); and James Flett, Assistant Administrator (Finance). Presidents of the Board, and hence Chairmen of the Management Committee, each serving two years during this period were A. N. Chown, Bruce Matthews, and Graham Thomson. They spent many hours month after month in committees considering administration problems and the future of the Hospital.

Miss Hazel Miller, who had been Director of Nursing since July 1958, left in 1960 to be married. Miss Olevia Wilson assumed the added responsibility of Acting Director of Nursing until Miss Sylvia Burkinshaw took over on 1 March 1961. Miss Burkinshaw received her training in Scarborough and London, England, and served in the Queen Alexandra Royal Naval Nursing Service. She received a Nursing degree from McGill and came to Kingston from the Hospital for Sick Children in Toronto.

The Kingston General Hospital School of Nursing celebrated its seventy-fifth anniversary in June 1961. Over two thousand young women had graduated from the School. The student body had grown from two to 176. Their training had become more intensive and more extensive; entrance qualifications had been raised and a full-time teaching staff operated the School. Yet many of the educational facilities were makeshift. They used classrooms and laboratories at Queen's until they could have others of their own. Plans for a Nursing Education Building awaited approval by the government. The building was started in 1963 and opened a year later to provide both educational and recreational facilities for the School of Nursing.

In 1961 there were 243 graduate nurses on staff at the Hospital. Their duties had developed over the years from a sort of glorified maid service to highly specialized nursing procedures. The less critical jobs of the nurses were taken over in 1961 by the first Certified Nursing Assistants, as many of their non-nursing duties had been assumed by Nurses Aides some years before.

Miss Olevia Wilson, after turning over her duties as Acting Director of Nursing to Miss Burkinshaw, retired as Assistant Superintendent of the Hospital in July 1961. She had served the Hospital for over forty years, many of them as a senior administrator. Her ability and her personality made staff, students, and patients remember her with respect and affection.

There was another retirement that year, of a man who had filled minor positions at the Hospital with a dedication prized in employees. John Hewetson, aged seventy-five, left the information desk in the main lobby. He had first come to the Hospital in 1911 as a porter. His duties then were to answer the one telephone, run the elevator, and help with the sweeping and dusting. After service in World War I and at Sydenham Military Hospital he returned to his old job at the Hospital. That job eventually became the information service, to direct visitors at the Hospital.

Among the senior administrators, Miss Elizabeth Gray replaced Mrs. Eileen Agardy as Director of Social Services. By 1961, that work had been extended so that one staff member worked in the Rehabilitation Service and another in the new Child Psychiatric Clinic. Mrs. Barbara Mutch became Director of Dietetics in January 1962. She enlarged the programme of education in her department, especially on-the-job training at all levels. Mr. J. R. Robson assumed administrative responsibility for Housekeeping and also for the Laundry and Linen Service. Miss Bertha Irvin retired after more than twenty-five years and John Stanton became Executive Housekeeper.

In 1962, Miss Lillian Gill retired after thirty-eight years' service at the Hospital. She had been Supervisor of the Isolation Hospital and later of the Bawden Wing. That year, 1962, the Hospital administration began recognizing the long service records of the many employees who had served the Hospital for twenty-five years or more. At a special social event a small presentation was made to each of these employees.

The Governors also started, with a luncheon party, to recognize formally the immense service of volunteer workers. The Women's Aid, with a membership of 527 in 1962, had been providing funds and volunteer service for the Hospital since 1905. Their financial assistance, derived mainly from their annual garden party and from their coffee and gift shop, helped a variety of projects at the Hospital and contributed substantial sums to the building fund. Volunteer service had grown over the years to become an important part of the Women's Aid activities. In 1962, over 300 of their members gave volunteer service to the Hospital. To recognize this important contribution to the operation of the Hospital, the Governors placed Mrs. Doris Brebner, Director of the Women's Aid Volunteer Service, on the regular staff of the Hospital.

In 1962, the Women's Aid sponsored a new group of volunteers. They were teenage girls, called Candy Stripers because of their pink and white striped pinafores. They helped to distribute menu cards, carried trays, and fed patients who were unable to feed themselves. By the middle of the decade a large group of these Candy Stripers had each given over 100 hours of volunteer service. It had started as a summer vacation operation but it grew to year-round volunteer service with each Candy Striper working after school, not more than two days a week.

The first half of the decade saw many changes in the Medical Staff. During 1960, Dr. W. A. Jones and Dr. S. W. Houston retired from the Queen's staff but continued in a consulting capacity at the Hospital. Dr. S. L. Fransman, who had joined the Radiology department in 1955, became head of that department. Dr. Harry Warner (McGill) replaced Dr. Houston on the Attending Staff in General Surgery. Dr. A. K. Wylie (Queen's and Edinburgh) joined the staff as Plastic Surgeon. The Attending Staff was further enlarged by the appointments of Dr. DeMargerie in Ophthalmology, Dr. Woolin in Radiology, and Doctors Leslie Valberg, George Mayer and John Fay in Medicine. Dr. A. W. Bruce (Aberdeen and Edinburgh), who had interned at the Hospital, returned to take charge of the Department of Urology. Dr. N. E. Berry had retired because of ill health.

With the expansion of departments which followed the opening of the Connell Wing, in 1960, there were changes in the staff at the Hospital and at the University. Dr. E. H. Botterell (Manitoba and Toronto) succeeded Dr. G. H. Ettinger as Dean of the Medical Faculty at Queen's University. He was appointed a member of the Honorary Consulting Staff at the Hospital. Eleven appointments were made in 1962 to the Attending Staff, including, among others, Dr. M. A. Simurda (Toronto), Dr. P. A. F. Morrin (Dublin), Dr. T. W. Challis (McGill), and Dr. R. F. Briggs (McGill and Toronto).

Dr. D. L. C. Bingham resigned as head of the Department of Surgery in 1962. Dr. R. B. Lynn served as Acting Head until Dr. J. R. McCorriston was appointed, in 1963, to head the department at Queen's and at the Hospital. Dr. McCorriston, trained at Queen's and McGill, came to Kingston from Montreal where he had been on the teaching staff at McGill and on the surgical staff at the Royal Victoria Hospital.

Some new services were made possible by the extra staff. Dr. David Rosen directed an Orthoptic Service staffed by Miss Jennifer Blatchford from the Moorfields Eye Hospital in London. For infants and children there was a new Premature

Nursery and a Child Psychiatric Clinic. Dr. M. W. Partington (London and Edinburgh) joined Dr. A. M. Bryans in directing the new Paediatric Research Laboratories which were assisted by funds from the Kingston Shrine Club.

Other new services were organized by the existing staff as space and equipment became available. Early in 1962 two such services were instituted. Dr. G. Malcolm Brown set up a Special Investigation Unit where patients were active participants in research programmes while being treated for whatever disease or injury they were suffering. The research observations were, of course, incidental to the care and treatment of the patient. Some of the projects in this unit were a study of the effect of different reducing diets on weight loss in obese patients, a study of patients with thyroid disorders, and a study of the effect of certain diets on the thickness of blood and on clotting time, to be carried out with patients suffering from hardening of the arteries. The Special Investigation Unit consisted of thirteen beds, a research diet kitchen on Douglas III, and separate laboratory facilities in Angada. Dr. Leslie Valberg assisted in the organization and operation of the Unit.

The renovation of the Douglas Wing made possible also the establishment of an Intensive Care Unit. The concept of a special area designed and equipped to serve the needs of acutely ill patients grew out of the development of complex equipment and the complicated and concentrated procedures as well as the constant supervision necessary in the treatment of critically ill patients. The types of patients admitted to the Intensive Care Unit included those having had major surgery, those with severe kidney, coronary or respiratory problems, and those with severe head injuries or other neurosurgical conditions. In 1963 a Renal Failure Unit including an artificial kidney, was developed in conjunction with the Intensive Care Unit, by Doctors A. W. Bruce, D. L. Wilson, and P. A. F. Morrin.

In 1961, a Department of General Practice was established under the direction of Dr. G. C. Lindsay. With that arrangement doctors who were family physicians but not certified specialists could be given Hospital privileges. And the Hospital's role as a community hospital was more firmly established.

The Medical Staff recommended, in 1961, that a thorough investigation of the intern training programme should be made by an outside consultant. There had been difficulty in attracting graduates of good quality and also the interns at the Hospital had expressed some dissatisfaction with the training programme. The custom of providing interns for the service of every physician who had patients in the Hospital gave the intern plenty of work but only marginal education. The Residents who worked in a unique, close relationship with the Attending Staff, alone received proper training. The Association of Canadian Medical Colleges and the College of Physicians and Surgeons began to be concerned about the quality of intern education. They encouraged a review of the programme, such as the one commissioned by the Kingston General Hospital.

That study, completed in 1962, surveyed the various medical teaching activities at the Hospital. It recommended the establishment of Clinical Teaching Units. This recommendation was immediately approved and then worked out over the next year by the Medical Staff of the Hospital and of Queen's. The slight change from the former teaching method involved the designation of a fixed number of beds in specific areas as teaching beds. The beds were set aside for patients, whether public or private, attended by the teaching staff who were also the Attending Staff.

There was no change so far as the patients were concerned. But as the staff of the teaching departments grew the number of clinical teachers soon outnumbered the other doctors on staff. There was a limited availability of beds to the doctors on the Associate and the Courtesy Staffs of the Hospital. However, affiliated teaching hospitals were required by the province to have an agreement with a university that a sufficient number of teaching beds be provided in order to produce well-qualified doctors.

Over the years it had been the Attending Staff (who also held teaching appointments at the University) who cared for the public patients. And the concept underlying the teaching of medical students and interns had been that public, not private, patients were the subjects for clinical practice. With the new hospital insurance programmes the number of public patients decreased sharply. Many of the private patients of the Attending Staff were then cared for by the teaching team. These patients were admitted to the reserved beds in the Clinical Teaching Units. Of course, the role which the University played in making the services of highly skilled medical personnel available to the region was acknowledged. Many of the specialists would not have been there if it had not been for the Hospital's affiliation with the University. And improvements in patient service went hand in hand with teaching and research. Another change was made in order to concentrate and improve the intern training programme. Intern services were henceforth available only to the clinical teachers.

Kingston General Hospital also provided improved facilities for the education of nurses in the new Nursing Education Building. And residence facilities for the nurses, the next urgent need, were on the drawing board. It was not, however, until the summer of 1967, that construction began on the Nurses' Residence. It was completed two years later. Approval for such capital projects depended on government approval of the plans and on the availability of government funds.

As each step in the physical expansion of the Hospital was approved a still further increase in space was planned by the Governors. And because of the co-operation of the University and the Hospital in the establishment of Clinical Teaching Units they were prepared for the recommendations coming out of the Hall Report. That Report of the Royal Commission on Health Services pointed out the need for radical changes in methods, facilities, and financing in the training of medical and para-medical personnel. The government of Ontario acknowledged the urgent need by proposing to expend some 114 million dollars for the purpose. To supplement these expenditures, the federal government established a Health Resources Fund of 500 million dollars for capital building grants to medical schools and affiliated hospitals. The Queen's Medical Faculty was mentioned as one to receive a special grant.

That special grant would be used to expand teaching and research facilities for medicine at the University and to expand and modernize the Kingston General Hospital. Queen's planned a new Health Sciences Centre. The Hospital planning firm had proposals ready, too. Plans announced by the Board of Governors of the Hospital in March 1965 for a new concept in its expansion brought a variety of reactions from governments and from the general public. The proposal to replace older sections of the Hospital with a modern tower building in connection with the proposed Queen's Medical Sciences Centre received approval in principle from the Ontario Hospital Services Commission in 1965. Reaction to the plan by local citizens was mixed. General approval for expansion and the city's pride in the Hospital and the Medical School were tempered by disagreement about the site plan.

The Hospital's site near the waterfront in a residential area made much lateral expansion impracticable. The Hospital was composed of a series of old and new buildings spread out in a complex with long connecting corridors. There were varying floor levels and long distances between key areas. A more compact hospital would be more efficient. But the expansion of the University had already created problems and controversy in the city about housing, parking, and taxes. Some vocal citizens and a few aldermen viewed the Hospital's expansion plans with alarm. The Board of Governors, H. P. Davis, President, decided that the Hospital's case should be presented to the citizens. An intensive public relations programme was carried on by the Hospital, directed by their new Publicity and Information Officer, Mrs. Faith Avis, to inform the public more fully of the implications of the plan and the part which the government played in it. The plan itself, at that time, existed only in broad, general terms; details would come later.

The Hospital and the Queen's Medical Faculty asked all their department heads to submit estimates for space requirements which would form the basis for future planning. But the development of the concept into concrete plans was not easily achieved. To gather teaching, patient care, research, and administration into one physical setting called for a careful study of space needs and, above all, for close cooperation to provide for the integration of those needs. The two partners had to reach an agreement, not only on matters of space but also on the more critical matter of control.

Planning for the future could not be allowed to interfere with the usual operation of the Hospital. While the Building Committee of the Board of Governors considered long range plans, other committees had more immediate problems. Constant pressure for expansion came from patients waiting to be admitted, from medical and nursing staff, and from supporting services. The government grants covered basic operating costs but the Board was constantly confronted with non-allowable expenditures which they had to meet from other funds. There was a continual need for private donations to supplement the operating grants. Only with that assistance could the Governors fulfil their obligation to provide the best possible medical service to patients in the area.

Significant increases in work loads were experienced in every department and the bed occupancy rate was generally eighty-nine per cent. But there was still room for improvement in reducing waiting lists and in speeding the admission of patients. Services were expanded as quickly as possible to cope with the demand.

The Medical Records Department was reorganized under Mrs. R. B. Steeds to make information more readily available to the doctors. In-patient and out-patient files were amalgamated; the stenographic pool was enlarged to speed the recording of data. By 1970, with Mrs. V. Early in charge, additional procedures had been transferred to Medical Records and the work, involving preparation, filing, retrieval, reports, and storage, taxed not only the staff but also the space. Careful study of the problems brought recommendations for development of a form which would enable reports and indices to be computerized. Charts were then microfilmed and dictating stations were established throughout the Hospital. The physical changes in the department disrupted the work but the improvements thus achieved relieved the pressure.

The overall increase in the use of diagnostic services was twenty per cent in one year and the growth continued. Clinical Laboratories experienced one of the largest increases. Staff expansion to meet the work load filled and crowded the available space. In 1966 Dr. R. H. More resigned as Chief of Pathology after making important contributions to the Hospital in both his professional and administrative posts. He and Dr. Kipkie had built up in the department a staff of highly qualified individuals, not necessarily pathologists but trained specialists who were in charge of each of the disciplines of the Clinical Laboratories. Dr. Nathan Kaufman (McGill) became Chief of Pathology in July 1967, with Dr. Kipkie serving as Director of the Clinical Laboratory in charge of surgical pathology.

By the end of the decade new equipment and the introduction of automated procedures in biochemistry and haematology allowed the Laboratories to provide results more quickly and to cope with the greatly increased number of tests. The professional staff, as in all other departments, had large responsibilities in the resident training programme and were also involved in active research. They had been training medical laboratory technologists under an apprentice system and were able to set up in 1968 a two-phase programme of training, with gratifying success.

Diagnostic X-ray also experienced significant and steady growth in the patient load so that the already crowded space made an addition imperative. Scanning work was moved to new rooms in Empire basement with an adjoining Hot Laboratory. In 1971 a new wing was added to the X-ray Department to give two new X-ray rooms, better facilities for the Residents training in Radiology, and a new out-patients waiting room.

The Department of Therapeutic Radiology combined with the Ontario Cancer Treatment and Research Foundation, Kingston Clinic, continued to register all cancer cases treated in the Hospital, the Clinic, and Hotel Dieu. By 1969 when the need for a self-care hostel facility associated with the Clinic was recognized by the Cancer Society, Kingston General Hospital was asked to provide a site for such a lodge. The planning then in progress for the Health Sciences Centre delayed for some time a decision on the exact site for a hostel. In 1971 contracts were let for site clearance and the new building will be started this year (1972). Dr. Ronald Burr, the first Director of the Kingston Clinic, retired in July 1971, continuing as consultant to the Clinic and the Hospital. Dr. Stewart Lott, of Johns Hopkins, was appointed Director of the Clinic and Head of the Department of Therapeutic Radiology.

New services were added. A mobile heart station was in use the day after it arrived at the Hospital in November 1965, to revive a heart that had failed during an operation. The heart station combined several pieces of equipment used for heart treatment into a compact and portable unit which could be moved easily and quickly to any location where it was needed. It was equipped to follow and record heart action and to administer electric shock to treat a heart that was failing or had stopped.

In 1965 a Newborn Treatment and Research Unit was established in Paediatrics under the direction of Dr. R. W. Boston (Queen's). The Premature Nursery, in conjunction with the Department of Obstetrics, gave special attention to premature infants. One research project developed into a Perinatal Intensive Care Unit and a highly trained staff with relatively little turnover contributed to the skilled operation of the unit.

In January 1970 a new Children's Outpatient Centre, for ambulatory care, was opened in the children's wing of the Hospital. By the end of that first year there had been 6,248 patient visits to the general clinic and to various specialty clinics in this Centre which were developed to meet particular and recurring needs. By the end of 1971 there were thirteen paediatric specialty clinics operating, as well as the daily general clinics conducted by the Queen's University Child Health Programme doctors, and the regular infant clinics.

After Dr. A. M. Bryans went on sabbatical leave, Dr. M. W. Partington was appointed first Acting Head and then in September 1971, Head of the Department of Paediatrics. Further development in Paediatrics, as in many other departments, would be greatly influenced by the development of plans for the Health Sciences Complex. The ultimate location and consolidation of all paediatric service in the area is to be at the Kingston General Hospital. However, the removal of Obstetrics to Hotel Dieu will necessarily separate the Neonatology service from its close connection with the Paediatrics Department.

In 1965, Dr. Edwin Robertson relinquished his administrative post and Dr. J. A. Low (Toronto) was appointed Head of the Department of Obstetrics and Gynaecology. An Ambulatory Service set up for patients in this department was an immediate success and its scope was further increased by the development of a Gynaecological Clinic under the direction of Dr. H. Gorwill. Patient visits in the Ambulatory Service increased from about 5,000 in 1969 to 7,837 in 1971. The undergraduate and full graduate programmes in this department provide an increasing, direct involvement of the medical student in clinical experience.

A Therapeutic Abortion Committee was established in 1971 following the passage of new legislation regarding abortions. As a consequence of the new regulations there was an immediate and substantial increase in the number of therapeutic abortions carried out in the Hospital. Important problems of patient counselling and follow-up are being developed in association with the Abortion Unit.

There were other changes as doctors moved away or retired. Dr. Leslie Valberg took charge of the Special Investigation Unit after Dr. G. Malcolm Brown left Kingston in 1965, to become head of the Medical Research Council in Ottawa. The clinical, laboratory, teaching, and research activities of the unit expanded so rapidly that it became necessary to concentrate the activities and set up a centre for more efficient operation. In April 1970, a Diagnostic Centre was opened on Empire I near the Admitting Office to establish some new and special diagnostic procedures. Within the year it had to be enlarged to take care of a forty per cent increase in the number of patients. The new Diagnostic Unit opened in January 1971 and by the end of the year had processed 10,571 out-patients and 1,604 in-patients. Minor renovations made space available for a centralized unit for gastro-intestinal procedures where the miniature camera proved to be extremely valuable in the early detection of ulcers and of stomach cancer. Research by members of the unit also benefited many clinical departments concerned in patient care.

Meanwhile the main responsibility for financing this special investigation and diagnostic unit was transferred from the Medical Research Council to the Ontario Hospital Services Commission although the Council and various external agencies continued to support the research carried on in the unit. The training of research fellows had become an important function of this unit along with the teaching and training of residents, interns, and clinical clerks in the investigation of patients with metabolic, renal, haematological, and gastroenterological disorders.

Dr. Bruce Young who had been head of the Department of Rehabilitation Medicine at the Hospital, returned to Toronto. In 1966, Dr. D. C. Symington, a graduate of Glasgow University, was appointed Chief of Rehabilitation Medicine at the Hospital and head of a new department at Queen's. Within a year a Regional Rehabilitation Centre was established at the Hospital but it was affected by budgetary stringencies and delays in the building programme not only at the Kingston General Hospital but also at St. Mary's of the Lake.

In 1968, the Queen's School of Rehabilitation Therapy, in association with the Hospital's Regional Rehabilitation Centre, was opened. Joint appointments by Queen's and the Hospital brought Muriel Driver and E. P. Walmsley to direct the training courses. The separation of the School and the Centre in different buildings caused problems in patient care and in teaching. There was the usual desperate need for more space. The planned development of various programmes in Rehabilitation, both clinical and teaching, progressed in spite of serious under-staffing. A Speech Therapy Unit offering clinical services, in-patient care, and consulting services in city and area schools became, in fact, a regional service. In August 1970, Dr. D. Hallauer became the first psychologist to be assigned full time to the Rehabilitation Department.

In every division of the Department of Rehabilitation Medicine the educational programme and constant review of the effectiveness of various programmes were carried on in conjunction with service to more and more patients. Within the Hospital the space problem was further complicated by the geographical separation of the various treatment areas. A few new facilities, such as the shop housing the prosthetics and Orthotics Division, which made possible additional services to patients, soon had waiting lists. A new field of service was the development of more out-patient programmes, and further cooperation with the community agencies involving counselling and home visits as well as the coordination of services. In spite of shortages of medical manpower and a higher turnover of staff, the department maintained its standard of service to patients and met its teaching responsibilities while looking forward to the proposed new facilities.

While studies and discussion of the master plan for the Health Sciences Centre were proceeding, some renovations and expansion were carried out to tide the Hospital over until new facilities would become available. In order that the diagnostic X-ray service might have the space it so desperately needed, a site had to be cleared for an extension to the Douglas Wing. That site was associated with a tragic summer in Kingston history. It contained the mass grave of some fifteen hundred Irish immigrants who had died in the typhus epidemic in Kingston in

1847. The grave was marked by the Angel of Resurrection monument, placed there in 1895, through the efforts of Archbishop J. V. Cleary. With the cooperation of the Roman Catholic Church, city and provincial authorities, and the Kingston Historical Society, the mass grave was moved and the monument rededicated in Kingston's St. Mary's Roman Catholic Cemetery in June 1966.

The Department of Ophthalmology which had suspended the Orthoptic Clinic because of space, staff, and financial problems, reactivated the clinic in 1970. At that time the financial support of the Orthoptic and Glaucoma Clinic was assumed by the Ontario Hospital Services Commission. By the middle of 1971 some new facilities made possible the expansion of the clinic under the direction of Dr. R. J. Perry.

The operation of this department, as of others, was on a cooperative basis with Queen's University and Hotel Dieu. Two members of the department, Dr. J. Morgan and Dr. W. E. Willis, had their headquarters at Hotel Dieu. Doctors Rosen, Pinkerton, Gauthier, McBroom, and Perry were at the Kingston General Hospital. The department offered special programmes of instruction beyond its regular teaching duties for residents, interns, and clinical clerks.

An Allergy Clinic directed by specialist Dr. James Day was the first service of its kind in the region. This Hospital clinic was the consultation and testing unit for all allergy cases referred from doctors in the area. It administered 2,327 treatments in the first year of operation and also contributed to teaching and to research projects in allergy and immunology.

In many instances specialized services grew out of already established units because of increased demand. The enlarged programme in Renal Dialysis led to the approval, in 1966, of a Regional Chronic Dialysis Unit at the Hospital. The unit was moved from the Intensive Care section and set up with four artificial kidneys, making service available around the clock to assist patients suffering from renal failure.

The rapid development of this programme led to a major event in 1968. On December 1st in the early hours of the morning, the first renal transplant done in this area was performed at the Kingston General Hospital. Dr. J. R. McCorriston was the chairman of the transplant group, made up of members from the Hospital, Queen's University and Hotel Dieu. Members of the Medical Staff involved in the operation were: Dr. J. R. McCorriston, Chief of Surgery; Dr. Andrew Bruce, Chief of Urology; Dr. R. B. Lynn, Surgeon in charge of Cardiovascular and Thoracic Surgery; Dr. Peter Morrin, in charge of the Renal Dialysis Unit; Dr. John G. Connolly of the Department of Urology; Dr. E. J. P. Charrette of the division of Cardiovascular and Thoracic Surgery; and Dr. David Dunlap of Anaesthesiology. The group had been preparing for such an occasion for over six months and the excellent teamwork resulted in a successful kidney transplant. It was a dramatic reminder to the citizens in the area of the high quality of medical service available to them at the Kingston General Hospital.

By 1970 the Renal Unit had developed a programme of home dialysis for patients with chronic kidney failure who did not wish to have a kidney transplant. Three patients were being treated outside of the Hospital in the first year of this programme. Four renal transplants were performed in 1970.

A comprehensive Family Care Unit, directed by Dr. R. W. Dingwall (Queen's), was opened in the Hospital in September 1967. It was a joint project of the Hospital and the Medical Faculty to interest medical students in family practice. The graduate programme in this unit was designed to lead to specialist certification in family practice. But the unit also served another purpose. There had been a sharp increase in the use of the Emergency Department for non-emergency cases, by families without a family doctor. The Family Care Unit was designed to serve especially these people in the community as well as to educate doctors for general practice. The unit was staffed by members of the departments of Medicine and of Paediatrics, including Dr. David Alexander (Edinburgh), Dr. Hans Westenberg (Amsterdam), and Dr. John Chesebrough (Queen's). In 1969, the Family Care Unit, then under the direction of Dr. J. B. Stalker (Toronto), was moved into the Anne Baillie Building and saw about 500 patients a month. As an outgrowth of this, a new teaching service in general medicine was introduced.

The growing emphasis on family care and a consolidation under general practice was partly a reversal of the long-time trend to greater specialization. It was also a recognition of the patient – not merely his disease or injury – but the whole person with family and social needs and responsibilities. The growth of the work of the Social Service Department was further evidence of medicine's increasing concern with the individual patient and his problems, both medical and social. A large staff under the direction of Miss Elizabeth Gray worked closely with patients in all areas of the Hospital.

In 1967 Canada celebrated the Centennial of Confederation. History became news. The Board of Governors decided that it was a most suitable time to remind the public of the role that the Kingston General Hospital played in the development of the community. Statistics proved its impact as a large business enterprise. The Hospital's contribution to the educational life of the region and to medicine through research were the subject of reports and publicity releases from the Public Relations Department of Mrs. Avis. In November 1967, the Hospital Archivist, Margaret Angus, organized a display entitled 'A Hospital's Life Story – Kingston General Hospital 1832–1967', which attracted community interest. A visual presentation of pictures, documents, and charts traced the history of the Hospital. Physical displays of equipment and nurses' uniforms presented a contrast between the old and the new. A father and son picture section showed the strong influence on the Medical Staff of family tradition. And long-time members of all groups operating the Hospital were honoured in a formal ceremony. Many citizens who saw the display gained a new appreciation of the magnitude of the Hospital's service and its contribution to the community.

The understanding support of the public was necessary to meet problems in the immediate future. Mr. MacIntyre, with his new title of Executive Director, emphasized in his annual report to the Board the urgent need for additional space to meet the increasing demands by patients, teachers, researchers, and by government. As he said, the Hospital was bulging at the seams and it would be only with difficulty and with tolerance and understanding that the quality of service could be maintained until new facilities were provided. It was evident that lack of space would continue to be a major administrative problem for years to come. When there was no more space in the main Hospital buildings some services were moved into buildings adjacent to the Hospital.

Mr. MacIntyre noted the appointment of Dr. T. J. Boag, trained in Liverpool, McGill, and Queen's, to replace Dr. Robin Hunter as Chief of Psychiatry. The department had increased over the years by strengthening some specialties. Dr. R. F. Briggs's appointment in 1962 marked the beginning expansion of both in-patient facilities and out-patient services for children. Further developments in clinical work, research and teaching made necessary an increase in staff. At the end of 1971 there were sixteen Psychiatrists on the Attending Staff with an equal number of residents.

Dr. J. D. Copping (Toronto), a medical practitioner and hospital administrator, took the post of Associate Director (Medical) in June 1967. He was to be responsible for certain service departments and to provide a closer liaison of Administration with the Medical Staff. On his departure in 1970, his duties were divided between Miss Burkinshaw, who was made Director of Medical Support Services, and Mr. F. Hughes, Director of Medical Services Administration.

The two hundred and eighteen members of the Medical Staff, in 1969, to quote Dr. Binhammer, President of the Medical Staff, ranged from 'the most "Sophisticated Specialist" to the many able "Family Physicians" serving the Kingston area'. Those doctors had, consequently, different medical interests in patient care, teaching, and research. The doctors who were not engaged either in teaching or research projects felt that the role of the Hospital as a community hospital was in danger as it was becoming increasingly difficult to find beds for their patients. They asked for some guarantee that the situation would not worsen and that future plans would recognize their needs. President J. A. Cunningham of the Board of Governors assured the doctors that the Kingston General Hospital would continue to be a community as well as a major teaching hospital. Dr. Leslie Valberg undertook a reassessment of the bed distribution and utilization. As a result of his study the Medical Staff emphasized the need for more beds to meet the needs of both the community and the Medical School.

There was a reorganization that year of the School of Nursing. Miss Valerie Martin, who had been appointed in 1966 as Associate Director of Nursing, was made Director of the School of Nursing. New government regulations required the separation of the School from the nursing staff at the Hospital. The 'two plus one' training programme was introduced. Student nurses spent most of their first two years in the classroom, going into patient areas only in planned assignments for clinical instruction. The third year of their training consisted of an internship in the clinical areas.

Clinical experience was given also to students of the Nursing Assistant Training Centre, of the Queen's University School of Nursing, and of the Kingston Psychiatric School of Nursing. Special tours and visits were arranged for students and observers from Hotel Dieu and the Brockville General Hospital. As these various educational programmes moved into clinical areas, many of the Hospital nursing staff were involved in teaching as well as in patient care. Major problems arose regarding the integration of the student nurses with the regular staff in order to make effective use of their service to the nursing department, especially during their intermittent periods in the clinical areas. Even the student nurse internship programme encountered difficulties.

On further evaluation of the programme, the staff of the School of Nursing decided that a straight two-year diploma course would be preferable to the 'two plus one'. This would avoid conflicts of interest, of responsibility, and of authority. The School of Nursing of the Kingston General Hospital, in 1970, deleted the internship year and offered a straight diploma course. In 1971, Miss Una Ridley was appointed the new Director of the School. The School of Nursing, in 1971, had a faculty of 18 full-time and three part-time teachers for 181 students.

In January 1969, the student nurses moved into their new residence. There were 245 single rooms in the high-rise building on the waterfront. An intercom system connected the rooms on the eleven floors. Besides conveniences such as laundry and a hair-dressing room, the nurses had lounges, a recreation room with a complete kitchen and three private 'date' rooms. With the deletion of the intern year and consequent smaller number in the School of Nursing some of the rooms in the new residence were made available to students in other training courses at the Hospital. In 1971 the residence was occupied also by Registered Nursing Assistants, laboratory, and X-ray technician students. The old Anne Baillie Building became the Intern Residence.

Miss Sylvia Burkinshaw became Director of Nursing Service at the Hospital. Her staff in 1968 included:

Registered nurses	266
Non-registered nurses	66
Registered nursing assistants	82
Nurses Aides	87
Orderlies	46
Ward clerks	28
Operating room technicians	7
Oxygen technicians	2
	584

Two years later Miss Burkinshaw was moved to the position of Director of Medical Support Services and Miss Johanna Plummer was appointed Director of Nursing Services. The discontinuance of the intern year for nursing students who had filled over sixty positions, had a direct effect on Nursing Service which then had a large scale staffing problem. This problem was further complicated by the multiplicity of highly specialized patient units requiring extra staff with special training.

The Hospital had offered in-service training for members of the nursing staff. The Nursing Liaison Committee recommended that selected registered nurses should be instructed to perform special procedures which had hitherto been considered a part of medical practice. That recommendation, enthusiastically welcomed and implemented, was, indeed, a good method of making better use of the quality of training which recent graduates of the School of Nursing were receiving. In this way a number of procedures were transferred, relieving the doctors of some services to patients which were time-consuming but relatively simple.

To assist in more accurate diagnoses the Hospital was adopting a number of new procedures, as well as refining others. For instance, in 1968, thirty-one different radio isotopes were used for diagnosis and treatment. Brain scans and lung scans were being used more frequently. And further investigative procedures concerned with thrombophlebitis and renal function were being developed by research.

Dr. M. L. Williams, of London, became Chief of the Department of Otorhinolaryngology in January 1969. He relieved Dr. James Purvis who had agreed, when Dr. Macpherson retired, to be acting head only until a permanent appointment could be made. Dr. Donald Hooper (Queen's 1955) was made a member of the attending staff in 1965. Dr. Williams set up a special unit for the diagnosis and treatment of hearing loss, an Audiology section with Miss Averil Eaton in charge. That unit made it possible to distinguish between physical hearing loss and psychological hearing loss, and served an increasing number of in-patients and out-patients. In 1971 approval was given for a full residency programme in Otolaryngology.

As there were several retirements near the end of the decade of men who had served the Hospital and Queen's for many years, the Medical Staff began the custom

of assembling to honour their retiring colleagues. On 1 July 1968, Dr. W. Ford
Connell retired as Head of the Department of Medicine at Queen's University and
at the Hospital. He continued to serve as a Medical Consultant on the Attending
Staff and as a Professor at Queen's. Dr. Connell had been a member of the
Hospital's Medical Staff since 1934, following a tradition set by his father, Dr.
W. T. Connell, from 1894 to 1950. Dr. Ford Connell, an outstanding teacher and
physician, made important contributions to medicine in cardiology. He developed
at Queen's and at the Hospital an excellent, highly regarded Department of
Medicine which played a major role in the undergraduate and postgraduate
training programme at Queen's University.

Dr. Edmund R. Yendt, succeeding Dr. Connell, became Chief of Medicine at
the Hospital and Head of the Department of Medicine at Queen's. Dr. Yendt, a
native of Ontario and a graduate of the University of Toronto Faculty of Medicine,
had been senior physician at the Toronto General Hospital. Two more new members of the staff of Medicine were Dr. M. Cohanin (Tehran) in the division of
Metabolism and Nephrology, and Dr. T. D. Kinsella (McGill) as Director of the
Rheumatic Diseases Unit. In 1970 Dr. A. D. Ginsburg, a specialist in Haematology,
joined the department and the next year Dr. M. Singer was appointed to the
Nephrology section.

The Cardiopulmonary Unit in Etherington Hall was expanded in 1970 and
gave increased facilities for cardiac and respiratory diagnostic and research procedures. Dr. R. D. Wigle joined the unit in 1971 to investigate acute and chronic
respiratory disease. The laboratory in this unit was used also by the division of
Cardiothoracic Surgery for the insertion of transvenous pacemakers. A pacemaker
clinic was operated from this unit with patients returning every three months to
have the function of the pacemaker units checked.

In September 1969, three doctors who had served the Hospital for many years
retired from the Medical Staff. Dr. Duncan W. Boucher (Queen's 1928) of the
Department of Surgery, had been at the Hospital for almost forty years. Dr. Presley
A. McLeod (Queen's 1926) and Dr. Gordon W. Mylks, Jr. (Queen's 1929) had
long been members of the staff of Obstetrics and Gynaecology. Dr. McLeod had
joined the teaching staff in 1929. Dr. Mylks, following in his father's specialty, had
been at the Kingston General Hospital since he returned from graduate work in
Dublin in 1933.

The Director of Pharmacy, Fred Buck, who had been an employee of the
Hospital for thirty-two years, retired in 1969. He was succeeded by Douglas Fraser
of Manitoba.

There were also changes in the senior administrative staff as the complexity of
administrative activities increased. James Flett was made Associate Director (Administration) to relieve the Director of daily supervision of the operation of the

Hospital. D. J. Maybee became Controller and W. H. Ellis, a professional engineer, served as Director of Plant until his sudden death in 1971. Frank Hughes was at first Director of Hospital Services and then, in 1970, Directors of Medical Services (Administration). N. Kasian's appointment in 1971 as Director of Hospital Services completed the administrative team.

Kingston General Hospital was growing every year as a business enterprise. In payroll, physical facilities, purchase of goods and services, and in number of employees, the Hospital was one of the largest enterprises of the city and region. At the beginning of 1972 there were over 1,500 full-time and 237 part-time and casual employees. By adding the students and house staff the number reached about 2,100. The Hospital budget had increased from $2,658,000 in 1957 to $9,250,000 ten years later. In 1971 it was $17,640,252. The statistics on the use of the Hospital during the 1960s and early 1970s indicate the place of the Kingston General Hospital in the community.

	1959	*1969*	*1971*
Patients admitted	13,678	16,361	17,350
Births	1,557	1,185	1,122
Patient days	149,337	187,551	187,432
Surgical operations	5,137	8,493	10,224
Outpatient & Clinic visits	18,891	39,332	63,644
Emergency visits	*	35,423	35,912
Laboratory tests	114,938	608,411	1,731,619
Laboratory units	*	2,367,248	10,699,966
X-ray examinations	14,970	59,687	70,128
Number of beds	473	592	589
Number of bassinets	40	44	44

Included in out-patient and clinic visits.

What those figures also indicated was the tremendous pressure on patient accommodation at the Hospital. Further pressure came from medical, para-medical, and teaching departments which all needed more space and better facilities. Meanwhile the government encouraged still more training programmes.

Through its training programmes for doctors, nurses, technicians, and other para-medical personnel, and in close cooperation with Queen's University, the Hospital played an important part also in the educational life of the city and indeed of the whole country. Many of these educational programmes, designed for interns and residents, appealed also to practising physicians. The regular monthly meetings, inaugurated by the Department of Medicine in February 1964, developed over the next few years into a full programme of continuing education. The Walter T.

Connell Memorial Lecture, first given in 1965, was the beginning of the Medical Lecture Series which brought many world-famous doctors to Kingston. In addition, the postgraduate lectures, special rounds, conferences, and seminars were all open to practising physicians in eastern Ontario.

The intern and resident training programme was improved, expanded, and intensified. And there were far more enrolled in the programme. In 1946, there had been fourteen interns and one resident on the House Staff. In 1962, there were sixty-six on the House Staff: eighteen junior rotating interns and forty-eight senior interns, assistant residents, and residents.

In 1969, the final year Queen's medical students became clinical clerks at the Hospital, to spend forty weeks acquiring clinical education in the Departments of Medicine, Surgery, Obstetrics and Gynaecology, Paediatrics, Psychiatry, and other clinical specialties. Some problems arose between medicine and nursing regarding realms of authority, duties and responsibilities until definite policies were set. Dr. H. G. Kelly was made chairman of the Committee on Medical Education which was responsible to the Medical Advisory Committee regarding all medical education at the Hospital, both undergraduate and postgraduate.

One ongoing problem in medical education was created by the changing policies and programmes in the provincial and federal bodies which exercised such strong control over the appointment and training of post graduate medical students. There was need also for a better method of dealing with problems of mutual interest regarding the Hospital's educational activities and those of the Queen's Faculty of Medicine. A formal educational sub-committee was considered a possible solution but the creation of such a body was delayed by the major problems involving the Health Sciences Complex.

The statistics for 1971 show that there were 65 final-year medical students serving as clinical clerks, 22 interns, and 132 residents at the Kingston General Hospital. Ten research fellows also held appointments at the Hospital. The research projects carried on at the Hospital contributed to the improvement of patient care and also to medical knowledge. In 1969, for instance, 91 research papers written by members of the Hospital Medical Staff were published in national and international medical journals. In 1971, 169 publications were listed in the annual report. And still more research projects were being carried on by the Medical Staff and the Research Fellows.

A Health Sciences Centre to house the Kingston General Hospital and the Queen's Medical Faculty seemed closer to realization in 1965 than it did in 1968 when S. E. Simonson, former construction manager of Expo '67, was appointed Project Administrator. The Province had given approval to the concept but the details of the plan were yet to be settled. Two approaches and two firms of architects made agreement by the partners very difficult.

The firm of Agnew, Peckham and Associates had been planners for the Hospital since 1958. The plan devised by this firm for the prospective expansion of the Hospital had been the basis for the Board of Governors' announcement in 1965 regarding a cooperative effort with Queen's University in providing modern, efficient facilities for teaching, research, and for patient care.

Queen's University also presented plans. In June 1966, the Queen's Medical Faculty Building Committee made a submission to the Ontario Coordinating Committee for Health Sciences. That brief covered all aspects of teaching and research in the Medical School and in the Hospital. It involved also the Hotel Dieu Hospital which had signed, in 1966, a formal affiliation agreement with the Queen's Medical Faculty. Correspondence between Dean Botterell and the government, concerning the brief, resulted in a commitment by the provincial government in 1967 to increase the number of active treatment beds in the Kingston General Hospital.

But these separate approaches to government resulted in misunderstandings on the part of the government and of the two partners. The Hospital could willingly accept a plan of physical integration with the Queen's Medical Faculty but was reluctant to relinquish any of the autonomy it treasured. The working out of the details of the new buildings would have to be done in close cooperation before a further approach to government was made.

The necessary cooperation was not achieved without a struggle. Yet the need for immediate and joint action was clear and urgent. The provision of government funds, absolutely essential for such an undertaking, depended on cooperation in the planning process. The Joint University-Hospital Liaison Committee asked Dr. J. D. Hatcher for Queen's and Dr. Stuart Vandewater for the Hospital, to accept the responsibility of producing for that committee an integrated space budget for the whole building. A Project Control office was established in March 1968, in charge of S. E. Simonson, assisted by Derek Finch and John Robson. Their job was to coordinate the planning and construction of the Health Sciences Centre. They assisted the two doctors in working out the space budget with the staff of the Queen's Medical Faculty and the Hospital.

The draft report was presented to the Joint Committee in October, the completed report in February 1969. But long before that, it was apparent that there would be no immediate need for specific plans of any kind. The federal government announced that expenditures of the National Health Resources Fund in any one year would be specifically limited. This was one measure in the attempt to curb inflation in the country. On 19 November 1968, the Hospital was notified that there would be a strict limit on the provincial funds available for health care in Ontario in 1969. A 'freeze' was placed on all plans not yet approved. Since details of the Kingston Health Sciences complex had not been submitted to government, it was caught in the 'freeze'. All planning came to a standstill. It meant an indefinite delay in the realization of the building. Years of planning resulted in no new buildings, and the inadequacy of space was desperate.

Regular operating funds for hospitals were also limited. Kingston General Hospital was notified that $500,000 had to be cut from its 1969 budget, and the squeeze was on. Thirty proposed appointments to new staff positions were postponed. Every department had to look at its budget to cut out all but absolutely essential purchases of new equipment. The budget was trimmed to fit the funds available.

Both government officials and the citizens were concerned about the rapidly rising costs of health care, as the Government was paying from the taxpayers' pockets. Some way had to be found to provide the same quality of care more economically. The existing methods underwent a careful examination. And the Health Sciences Centre for Kingston, estimated at $80 million, did not fit into an economy budget. Governments who would provide the funds decided that unnecessary duplication of services had to be avoided, not only between the two partners but also in the whole area which had a number of hospitals. Careful regional planning would be the answer.

Some such planning had already been put into effect. A Regional Public Health Unit had been established in Kingston. And, in 1968, a Regional Ambulance Service was instituted as a cooperative effort. The service was financed by the provincial government by arrangement with one hospital – and only one hospital – in a region. By an agreement between the Kingston General Hospital and Hotel Dieu the ambulance service was based at Hotel Dieu. A joint committee of the two hospitals recommended policy matters regarding the service to their respective Boards for approval. The service was greatly improved through the interest and efforts of Dr. W. R. Ghent, as Chief of Surgery at Hotel Dieu, a member of the Consultant Staff at Kingston General Hospital, and an Associate Professor of Surgery at Queen's.

Another development in coordination was the formation of a Regional Laundry Board. Representatives from St. Mary's of the Lake Hospital, Ongwanada Sanatorium, the Lennox and Addington County Hospital, and the Kingston General Hospital were incorporated as Kingston Regional Hospital Laundry, Inc. The Hotel Dieu administration deferred joining until a settlement could be reached on new laundry equipment which Hotel Dieu had just purchased. Kingston Regional Laundry, Inc. planned to build and operate one laundry which would service a number of hospitals. Government funds were available to assist such a venture in cooperation.

Regional planning, however, or even cooperative planning, was progressing very slowly on the biggest project – the Health Sciences Centre, and a coordination of hospital services in the area. The new Principal of Queen's University, John J. Deutsch, who took office in October 1968, thought that strong and positive action was necessary to cut through the maze of proposals and counter proposals then before the planners. The Board of Governors of the Kingston General Hospital agreed. Unless positive, concerted action was taken quickly, the government funds for the project might not be available.

Consequently, late in 1968, representatives from all the hospitals in Kingston and representatives from Queen's University met and declared themselves in favour of the formation of a Regional Hospital Planning Council. Early in 1969, the Queen's University and Affiliated Hospitals Council – QUAFHOP – was formed to coordinate planning and to make joint representations to government about the Health Sciences network of institutions which would be associated with the Queen's Faculty of Medicine. QUAFHOP would also be involved in the planning for the building, the actual physical facilities proposed for the Hospital–Queen's site.

When government officials met with the Council in March they agreed that a coordinated study was necessary. A firm of planners, not previously involved with either the Hospital or the University, was hired. Llewelyn-Davies, Weeks, Forestier-Walker and Bor of London, England and of Ottawa, were asked to conduct the study in the shortest possible time. There was a crucial need for new facilities. QUAFHOP was, therefore, anxious to obtain government approval to proceed with some work as soon as possible.

The consulting firm presented its report in July 1969. It recommended the integration of all area hospital services, stating, 'We believe that integration of the three main components (Queen's Medical School, Kingston General Hospital and Hotel Dieu) into an integrated complex is the preferred course, providing it can be initiated quickly and accomplished in a reasonable (say five to eight) span of years. As a second alternative, and accepting that costs will be higher to the community, a federated Centre would be a viable proposition given a strong coordinating structure to plan and operate the units in a complementary way.'

They recommended the development of the Health Sciences complex on the designated site on the waterfront. The successful operation of a Health Sciences Centre, the Report said, 'can only be achieved in full by yielding a significant measure of individual autonomy ... the coordination and cooperation to be demanded is tantamount to the merging of these organizations under one unified super-management with the University Health Sciences.'

The way had to be worked out and far-reaching decisions had to be made before approval and financial support would be available from the governments. The attitude of the Hospital was shown in the report at the end of 1969, presented by John J. MacKay, President of the Board of Governors of the Kingston General Hospital.

Until recently, the hospital in Canadian society was a relatively autonomous institution. Each hospital made individual decisions and developed according to individual plans. In urban centres this resulted in the development of a number of general hospitals, each duplicating the services offered by the others. Health care in Canada has now reached a high degree of sophistication and each citizen expects quality health care as a right. It has become increasingly evident that it is economically impossible to sustain the existing health care system with its wasteful duplication of services.

Regional planning must now take place, with each region setting up an economically sound, community-service oriented system for the delivery of health care. Unilateral decisions will no longer be possible. Each hospital will have to assess its logical role in the total community picture.

In our community, we have a great asset in the presence of the Queen's University medical school, a factor which brings to our hospitals an added responsibility to participate in medical education and in medical research. It also brings to our community a large number of highly-qualified specialists, making available to patients in this region a very high quality and wide variety of medical services.

The hospitals of Kingston – Kingston General Hospital, Hotel Dieu Hospital, St. Mary's of the Lake Hospital, and the Kingston Psychiatric Hospital – together with Queen's University, last year formed the QUAFHOP Council (The Queen's University and Affiliated Hospitals Council). The Council is confronted with the task of creating an executive and administrative organization for a regional health sciences complex at Kingston.

. . . I believe that we are developing an organization that will serve Eastern Ontario well and, for that reason, our Board has worked hard and we will continue to bend our efforts toward achieving the best possible arrangement for total community health care.

At the end of 1969, the government granted approval for the Kingston General Hospital to call for tenders for the construction of additional floors on the Walter T. Connell Wing. The addition would provide space for patient beds during the redevelopment, stage by stage, in the older parts of the Hospital.

In November 1971 the new floors of the Connell Wing were officially opened. One was devoted entirely to storage and extensive services. The ninth floor was for medical patients. The new Connell Coronary Unit on the tenth floor, generously supported by the Connell family, was named in honour of Dr. W. Ford Connell for his great contributions to coronary care and research. At the same time an announcement was made about the establishment of the W. Ford Connell Heart Fund to promote patient care, teaching, and research by members of the Department of Medicine at Kingston General Hospital.

This construction did not add any patient beds to the Hospital's total but provided a modern and efficient patient care area to replace some very old and outmoded facilities. The Nickle Wing (1891) ended its career as an in-patient area to be used temporarily for Out-patient Clinics during renovation on Connell I. It then was used for administrative offices, being slated for demolition if and when the Health Sciences building was constructed.

The next most urgently needed building was one to house the Ambulatory Clinics but nothing could be done until the government gave its approval to the whole concept of the Health Sciences Centre. QUAFHOP, the loose voluntary coalition of the University and each of the affiliated hospitals was making some progress in planning but much more was necessary very soon.

An equitable and acceptable division of services between the hospitals and a workable combination of patient care facilities had to be coordinated with teaching and research facilities for the University. That was difficult but even more so was general agreement on the form of a central body, a successor to QUAFHOP, which could deal with the cooperative planning and coordinated development. Neither of these needs could be easily achieved in a group of organizations most of which counted well over 125 years of struggle to maintain not only their identity but often their very existence. Their indecision and failure to agree cast doubts on whether differences could be resolved and the necessary agreement achieved.

The setting up of an administrative central organizational structure was the first objective. In 1971 the firm of Booz, Allen and Hamilton, Canada, presented to QUAFHOP recommendations for such a structure. Their report suggested five possibilities ranging from a concept of total independence for each institution to total fusion. Neither of these extremes seemed acceptable. Agreement was finally reached for a concept of 'moderate association'. The consultants, so President Harvey Millman reported to the Board of Governors in March 1972, described this 'moderate association' concept as one which brings the 'individual organizations and the central organization to a point of balance in authority and responsibility in the major areas of facilities, programmes, finances and manpower.' Facilities planning and programme planning would be delegated to the central organization. The responsibility for day-to-day operations would be left with each institution and title to assets would remain with each institution. The new council would perform a review function on operating budgets with a view to coordinating activities and programmes. With this arrangement, unnecessary duplication of facilities could be effectively eliminated.

The decision to surrender certain autonomy was not an easy choice, but, having made that choice, QUAFHOP agreed that in order to carry into effect the 'moderate association' concept it would be necessary to deal immediately with two major items which required formal agreement by all members. The first was a partnership agreement, embracing all members of QUAFHOP, that would set, among other things, the representation of each institution to the newly created council. The second was a financial plan that would discharge the community obligation for the contribution of funds to the overall development. QUAFHOP appointed two sub-committees to deal with the two issues.

The sub-committee for the partnership agreement attempted to reach broad agreement on the powers, functions, and duties to be delegated to the new central authority. At the same time they discussed a functional plan which would be part of the partnership agreement. Several drafts were considered and agreement was finally reached on 18 January 1972. It was a proposal to set up a legal successor to QUAFHOP with designated membership, functions, powers, and duties in order to provide policy direction for the development and ongoing administration of the complex. The chairman of QUAFHOP, Principal John J. Deutsch, forwarded the agreement to the provincial authorities on 16 February 1972.

The second part of the agreement, prerequisite to any provincial approval, concerned the financial plan. The total cost of the complex, including the proposed developments at the Hotel Dieu and St. Mary's of the Lake, was estimated at $106 million. Of this amount, $80 million would be received in outright grants for teaching and research that included some service elements. The balance of $26 million, designated as conventional hospital financing, would have two components: two-thirds from a grant known as Community Financial Assistance Funds and one-third from community sources (approximately $8 million).

The proposed method for raising the community contribution was considered by the sub-committee. It became apparent that the ability to contribute cash varied with each institution and some cooperation would be necessary to resolve the problem. The sub-committee formulated a plan, the terms of which could be met by all participants, in which Queen's University agreed to contribute a substantial amount to the total required from the community. The University had no real obligation in this respect since their contribution was channelled entirely through the Health Resources Fund and represented $80 million in total. As a result of these negotiations the plan was finally agreed upon. It is planned to raise $2,500,000 from a proposed campaign to commence in 1976. The contribution of the Kingston General Hospital amounts to $840,000 spread out over the years 1972 to 1978.

An immediate building project, the proposed parking garage on the lower campus of Queen's University is urgently needed to provide parking facilities for the proposed complex. Since the government does not provide funds for parking, Kingston General Hospital and Queen's have to borrow funds for construction costs, and repayment of the borrowed funds must be met from parking charges. The operating costs and any other charges can only be recovered from the people who use the facility, mainly patients, visitors, or employees of Kingston General Hospital.

President Millman concluded his report to the Board of Governors as follows:

Those directly involved in the delivery of health care are now taking the view that we will have in reality one general hospital to serve Kingston and the region. The specialized skills that are available, together with highly specialized equipment, make Kingston a natural referral centre for eastern Ontario. Each institution would contribute in its own special way. In an atmosphere of joint effort, the skills and talent available can be more effectively dispensed. Clearly no one hospital can provide superb technical-medical service in every area. Enlisting the resources of all hospitals has the potential of making the best services available to all. We recognize that this new approach is not free of criticism, and we have the usual skepticism that goes with change, but we are confident that this is the proper course to take.

The Kingston General Hospital, 150 years after the government granted £3,000 to aid in the erection of a hospital in or near Kingston, is about to become an integral part of a $106 million complex. The suggestion of a regional hospital scheme, made by R. F. Armstrong in a 1952 speech to the Kiwanis Club, is twenty years later about to become a reality.

The history of the Kingston General Hospital is not unique as the story of a hospital's struggle to make progress in health care, education, and research. Every hospital wages the annual contest between revenue and expenditure. But this Hospital is unique in being a teaching hospital in a small city resisting the pressures to move the teaching to a larger centre where there would be more doctors, more patients, and more variety in clinical material. And although the Hospital is not, strictly speaking, a university hospital, it is the major teaching hospital for Queen's. The Queen's Medical Faculty and the Hospital have always had a close link since each is dependent on the other. And each seems to have a similar philosophy of maintaining quality while limiting quantity.

Yet, necessarily, they have different viewpoints. Queen's, beginning as a college to educate young men who might go into the Presbyterian ministry, started the Medical Faculty in inauspicious circumstances, on a one-year trial basis, mainly because of a religious restriction in a Toronto medical school. Today Queen's main concern with the Hospital is as a clinical laboratory for students and a research facility for staff.

Kingston General Hospital, on the other hand, started through popular demand on a completely ecumenical basis to provide a charity hostel for the sick poor. It was and continues to be a community hospital and its community has grown over the years to encompass the entire Eastern Ontario region. It is equally evident that the Hospital has a tremendous advantage in being so closely connected with the Queen's Medical Faculty. Not only does the Queen's connection assure that highly skilled specialists are on the Hospital Attending Staff but it has also provided, for many years, the channel through which the most certain and largest grants of government funds come to the Hospital.

When the Hospital was established the financial responsibility rested mainly on private charity. A group of citizen volunteers was concerned in the most minute details of hospital administration and doctors volunteered their services to give free medical care to the sick poor. At that time the Hospital admitted charity cases only.

But charity could be obscured and sometimes lost in plain economics. As patient numbers increased it became necessary to have a surer source of income than humanitarian impulses of a small group of citizens. Kingston General Hospital became a haven for more than the sick poor as medical discoveries made possible the control of epidemics and infections. The development of medical knowledge and skills and the growth of the importance of hospitals in medical care and medical education parallelled the progressive transfer of financial responsibility for health care from the private to the public sector.

With the growth of government responsibility for medical care the patient was removed from contact with administration; it was easier to be impersonal, to deal with statistics, rather than with an individual on a personal basis. The development of medical specialties and consequent fragmentation of treatment furthered the impersonal trend in health care. Yet a shift has begun: the establishment of family care units, the training of general practitioners, the emphasis on the social service aspect in hospital care, and, more recently, the recommendation that hostels and even home care might be better in some cases for both patient and hospital.

In the development of the Health Sciences Centre, the historic buildings of Kingston General Hospital may disappear but the dedication to patient care, medical education, and medical research will become even stronger than ever.

Eleventh Parliament – Chap. xxviii 2nd Year William iv A.D. 1832
Chap. xxviii.

An Act granting to His Majesty a sum of money in aid of the erection of an Hospital in or near the Town of Kingston. Passed 28th. January 1832.

Most Gracious Majesty.

Whereas it is necessary to provide for the erection and establishment of an Asylum for the destitute sick within this Province: And Whereas the inhabitants of the Town of Kingston have subscribed a large sum of money towards the erection of an Hospital in or near that place, and have prayed that an additional sum may be granted from the Public Revenues in aid of that object; may it please Your Majesty that it may be enacted. And be it therefore enacted by the King's Most Excellent Majesty, by and with the consent of the Legislative Council and Assembly of the Province of Upper Canada, constituted and assembled by virtue of and under the authority of an Act passed in Parliament of Great Britain, entitled 'An Act to repeal certain parts of an Act passed in the fourteenth year of his Majesty's Reign, entitled "An Act for making more effectual provision for the Government of the Province of Quebec, in North America, and to make further provision for the Government of the said Province" – and by the authority of same' – That from and out of the Rates and Duties raised, levied and collected, or hereafter to be raised, levied and collected, there be granted to His Majesty, His Heirs and Successors, the sum of Three Thousand Pounds of lawful money, which said sum of Three Thousand Pounds shall be applied in aid of the erection and completion of an Hospital in or near the Town of Kingston for the destitute sick: Provided always, that the said sum of Three Thousand Pounds shall be advanced and paid by equal installments of One Thousand Pounds – the first instalment to be advanced and paid on the first day of May next after the passing of this Act, and the two remaining instalments on the first day of May in each of the two succeeding years.

(ii) And be it further enacted *by the authority aforesaid, that John Macaulay, James Sampson, and Edmund Westrop Armstrong, all of Kingston aforesaid, be Commissioners for superintending and managing the erection and completion of the said Hospital, and for the purchasing or otherwise obtaining, choosing and determining the site thereof.*

(iii) And be it further enacted *by the authority aforesaid, that the said sum of Three Thousand Pounds shall be paid by the Receiver General of the Province in discharge of such Warrant or Warrants as shall from time to time be issued by the*

Governor, Lieutenant Governor or person administering the Government of the Province, and shall be accounted for to His Majesty, His Heirs and Successors, through the Lords Commissioners of His Majesty's Treasury for the time being, in such manner and form as His Majesty, His Heirs and Successors, shall be pleased to direct.

Chapter cⅢ Victoria 12 v 1849
An Act to incorporate the Trustees of the Kingston Hospital
30th. May 1849

Whereas the inhabitants of the City of Kingston and the Midland District being from their position constantly called upon to supply necessities and relieve the condition of sick and destitute Emigrants and other transients and the mariners of the Lakes, it is most desirable that the Hospital at Kingston should be incorporated in order that it may be conducted in a more efficient manner: And whereas the Parliament of the late Province of Upper Canada, in the second year of His Majesty's Reign, did pass an Act granting three thousand pounds in aid of the erection and completion of a hospital in or near the Town of Kingston for the reception of the destitute sick, in the Preamble of which Act it is stated 'That the inhabitants of the Town of Kingston have subscribed a large sum of money towards the erection of an Hospital in or near that place': And whereas by the said Act, three commissioners were appointed for superintending and managing the erection and completion of the said Hospital and for purchasing the site thereof, and who did afterwards proceed to erect the said Hospital: And Whereas in the seventh year of his said Late Majesty's Reign, the said Parliament did grant a further sum of five hundred pounds for furnishing and fitting up the said Hospital; which was expended for the purpose: And whereas the said Commissioners have discharged their duty the erection, finishings and fitting up of the said Hospital, it is proper to relieve them of their charge and to establish a Corporation, to be composed as hereinafter provided for the better management and disposition of the lands and property now and hereafter to be held in trust for the said Hospital, and for the better management of any portion of the Marriage License Fund which may be appropriated by the Governor to the said Hospital under the statute of this Province passed in the ninth year of Her Majesty's Reign, entitled, 'An Act to provide for the payment of certain Rebellion Losses in Lower Canada, and to appropriate the proceeds of the Marriage License Fund,' and to make such Rules and By-laws for the internal or other management and regulation of the said Hospital as shall from time to time seem to them expedient and necessary. Be it therefore enacted by the Queen's Most Excellent Majesty, by and with the advice and consent of the Legislative Council and of the Legislative Assembly of the Province of Canada, constituted and assembled by virtue of and under the authority of an Act passed in the Parliament of the United Kingdom of Great Britain and Ireland entitled 'An Act to reunite the Provinces of Upper and Lower Canada, and for the Government of Canada', and is hereby enacted by the authority of the same – That the Mayor of the City of Kingston for the time being, the Judge of the Midland District Court for the time being, the Warden of the Midland District for the time being, the Sheriff of the Midland District for the time being, and three such Aldermen of the City of Kingston as shall from time to time as hereinafter mentioned be elected, for the purpose by the City Council of the said City, shall be a body corporate by the name of the Trustees of the Kingston Hospital, and as such shall have perpetual succession and a common seal, and have and hold all such land as is now attached or adjacent to the said Hospital or in connection therewith; and shall be capable of receiving, taking and holding from Her Majesty, or from any person or persons or any body corporate or politic, by grant devise or otherwise, any land or interest in lands, or any goods, chattels, or effects which Her Majesty, or any such person or persons, body corporate or politic, may be desirous of granting or conveying to them for the use and support of said Hospital, or the endowment thereof; and also shall and may from time to time by such by-laws and rules for the admission into, and internal management and regulation of the said Hospital or for the leasing or management of such of the lands or property of the said Hospital as may not be required for the immediate use thereof, as shall to them be meet and expedient: Provided always that such by-laws and Rules shall be laid before the Governor General, or Person administering the Government of this Province in Council, within thirty days after same shall have been made and adopted, and may be by him disallowed within one month after same shall be transmitted to him by the Trustees.

(II) And be it enacted – *That it shall be lawful for the said City Council of the City of Kingston, immediately after the passing of this Act, and thereafter in the month of January in each and every year beginning with the year one thousand eight hundred and fifty, to elect any three of the aldermen of the said City to be trustees under this Act, and the aldermen at any time so elected, or the survivor or survivors of them shall continue in office as such Trustees until the month of January next following their election, or until the election of their successors as aforesaid, which ever event may soonest happen.*

(III) And be it enacted, *That any four of such Trustees shall form a quorum for the transaction of business.*

(IV) And be it enacted – *That the said Trustees shall have power to appoint a Clerk or Secretary, who shall keep regular minutes of their proceedings, and such other officers for the proper management of the Hospital as they shall consider proper and to remove him, her, or them, at pleasure, and appoint others in their places.*

(v) And be it enacted – *That it shall be the duty of the said Trustees to place in good safe and sufficient securities, all moneys which may at any time come into their hands for the use and support of the said Hospital, which may not be required for the immediate expenditure of same, and from time to time, when required to do so by the Governor General, or Person administering the Government in Council, to render an account in detail of all monies received by them as Trustees, specifying the sources from which the same have arisen or been received, and the manner in which the same have been invested or expended, and all such particulars as may be necessary to show the state of the funds or endowment, if any of the said Hospital, and the said Trustees shall also lay an annual statement of their affairs before the Houses of the Legislature, within thirty days after the commencement of each Session.*

(vi) And be it enacted – *That the said Trustees by the name aforesaid, shall have power to sue in any of the Courts of this Province having competent jurisdiction for any cause of action touching the property of the said Trustee, or for any monies due or payable to them or their predecessors, for the rent or rents of any lands or buildings, or on any other account whatever, and to distrain for rents when same are in arrears and unpaid, and to act in all matters touching the collection and control of the funds of the said Hospital and the management and disposition of any lands belonging to the same, as to them or a majority of them shall appear most conductive to the interest of their trust, and no individual of the said Trustees shall be held responsible for any act or acts of the said Trustees which shall be done or determined upon at any meeting at which he shall not have been present, or from which he shall dissent provided such dissent be entered and signed by him on the minutes to be kept aforesaid.*

(vii) And be it enacted – *That it shall and may be lawful for any Medical Student in the said City of Kingston, to visit the wards of the said Hospital and attend them upon the payment of such fees, and under such regulation and instructions as the said Trustees shall and may by any by-law from time to time direct and appoint.*
Further amended, 1856 (19–20 Victoria ch. 107) and 1897 (60 Victoria, ch. 101).

Chairmen and Presidents of the Board of Governors of
Kingston General Hospital

MAYORS OF KINGSTON:

1849 to 1856	Francis M. Hill	1928	H. W. Davis
	John Counter	1931	R. E. Burns
	John Flanigan	1933	W. T. Minnes
	O. S. Gildersleeve	1935	R. G. H. Travers
1857	James Sampson, M.D.	1937	J. S. Crawford
1862	Thomas Kirkpatrick	1939	M. B. Baker
1866	Horatio Yates, M.D.	1941	E. W. Waldron
1882	Orlando S. Strange, M.D.	1943	Elmer Davis
1890	George A. Kirkpatrick	1945	T. A. Kidd
1893	E. J. B. Pense	1948	P. H. Swalm
1895	John Duff	1950	A. L. Davies
1899	E. H. Smythe	1953	D. J. Rankin
1902	John Marshall	1955	Stuart Polson, M.D.
1904	D. M. McIntyre	1957	R. C. Oaks
1906	G. Y. Chown	1959	A. N. Chown
1908	R. H. Duff	1961	B. W. Matthews
1910	James Minnes	1963	G. G. Thomson
1912	F. C. Lockett	1965	H. P. Davis
1914	A. F. Chown	1967	J. A. Cunningham
1916	R. E. Kent	1969	John MacKay
1925	H. C. Nickle	1971	H. L. Millman

Members of the Board of Governors

1856 LIFE GOVERNORS

Dr. James Sampson
John A. Macdonald
Thomas Kirkpatrick
James Hopkirk
John Paton

John Macaulay
John R. Forsythe
John Watkins
Thomas Askew
William G. Hinds

James Harty

1969 LIFE GOVERNORS

A. L. Davies   H. W. Davis   T. A. Kidd

Ex officio   eleven

Subscription Governors   one hundred thirty-seven

From these are chosen:

THE MANAGEMENT COMMITTEE

J. J. MacKay, *Chairman*
H. L. Millman, *First Vice Chairman*
J. D. Lee, *Second Vice Chairman*
J. A. Cunningham, *Past President*
Dr. R. W. Dingwall, *President of the Medical Staff*
Dr. J. A. Low, *Chairman of the Medical Advisory Committee*
Dr. J. J. Deutsch, *Principal of Queen's University*
D. M. MacIntyre, *Executive Director and Secretary*

C. J. Bermingham
H. H. Blakeman
M. L. Davies
H. P. Davis
R. A. Little

Dr. W. A. Mackintosh
L. G. Macpherson
A. D. McGinnis
P. G. D. Swan
Col. T. A. Kidd

Superintendents of Kingston General Hospital

1887–1891	Dr. Ephraim Hooper		Dr. M. F. Coglin
1891–1896	Dr. Roland K. Kilborn	–1916	Dr. J. R. Boyd
1896–1900	Dr. James Third	1916–1918	Dr. J. C. Wright
1900–1903	Dr. Andrew Haig	1918–1920	Dr. D. C. Matheson
1903–1904	Miss Elizabeth Flaws	1920–1923	Dr. A. E. Ross
1904–1906	Miss Elizabeth C. Gordon	1923–1923	Dr. J. H. Pilkey
1906–1908	Dr. A. D. MacIntyre	1923–1924	Mr. Frank Taylor
1908–1915	Dr. H. A. Boyce	1925–1958	Mr. R. Fraser Armstrong
1915	Dr. D. A. Coon	1958–1972	Mr. D. M. MacIntyre

Head Nurses and Superintendent of Nurses
Kingston General Hospital

1886–1886	Miss Steele	1908–1908	Miss Bertha Pickles
1886–1887	Miss Underhill	1908–1912	Miss Bertha Willoughby
1887–1892	Miss Margaret McMillan	1912–1912	Miss Lydia Elmsley
1892–1893	Miss Helen Urquhart	1912–1920	Miss Claudia Boskill
1893–1895	Miss Emily Macdonell	1921–1924	Miss Patience Carey
1896–1897	Miss Helena MacMillan	1924–1942	Miss Anne Baillie
1897–1899	Miss Alice Taylor	1942–1958	Miss Louise Acton
1899–1904	Miss Elizabeth Flaws	1958–1960	Miss Hazel Miller
1904–1906	Miss Elizabeth C. Gordon	1960–1961	Miss Olevia Wilson
1906–1907	Miss Lizzie Tyson	1961–1971	Miss Sylvia Burkinshaw
1907–1908	Miss Alice Scott		

Building Chronology

1835	Main Building	1925	Douglas Building
1862	Watkins Wing	1925	Richardson Laboratories
1891	Nickle Wing	1927	Nurses' Home
1894	Doran Building	1947	Victory Wing
1895	Fenwick Operating Theatre	1953	Angada Children's Hospital
1903	Nurses' Home (Later Anne Baillie)	1959	Etherington Hall
1914	Empire Wing	1960	Dietary Wing
1923	City Isolation Hospital	1960	Walter T. Connell Wing
	(Later Bawden)	1964	Nurses' Education Building
1923	Heating Plant	1969	Nurses' Residence
1923	Service Building		

Comparative Figures

	1849	1969
Institutional Establishment	1 building 50 beds	19 buildings 636 beds
Patients	225	17,546
Out-patients	?	74,755
Value in buildings and equipment	Approx. $18,000	$16,618,272
Current revenue	£300 plus donations	$13,672,717
Expenditures		
Salaries and wages	£380	$ 9,837,141
Other	?	$ 3,948,751
Employees	3	1,794
Medical Staff		
Clinical clerks	nil	65
Interns	nil	18
Residents	1	119
Honorary	nil	21
Consultant	2	8
Attending	3	120
Associate	nil	47
Courtesy	nil	51

The records of the Kingston General Hospital have been the main source material for this history. An almost uninterrupted series of reports, minutes, and other records has made the task of research simple in search but extensive in reading and somewhat difficult in selection. A most remarkable accumulation of early records formed the basis for the present extensive collection of historical material in the Hospital Archives.

Others before me have collected material and some have also written brief histories of the Hospital. Dr. Thomas Gibson's collection is in the Queen's University Archives. Dean N. F. Dupuis and Dean J. C. Connell both wrote short accounts. The large amount of material collected by Hugh C. Nickle was especially helpful in the story of the School of Nursing. Edwin Horsey's unpublished manuscript history of the Hospital to 1938 demonstrated his painstaking search of early records. Mrs. Mary C. Campbell's *History of the Women's Aid* should be read as a supplement to this history.

Primary Sources

KINGSTON GENERAL HOSPITAL ARCHIVES
Admission Ledger, Annual Reports, Board of Governors' Minutes, Cash Books, Death Book, Management Committee Minutes, Medical Board Minutes, Policy Statements, Visitors' Book, Special Studies and Reports.

ONTARIO ARCHIVES Macaulay Papers

PUBLIC ARCHIVES OF CANADA Legislative Journals, Public Works Papers, Secretaries' Letter Books.

QUEEN'S UNIVERSITY ARCHIVES Gibson Collection, Nickle Papers, Medical Society Minutes, Women's Medical College Papers.

KINGSTON NEWSPAPERS 1810–1971

Secondary Sources

ANDERSON, H. B. 'The Evolution of Medicine in Ontario', *Canadian Practice and Review*, 31 (1906), 673.

ANGUS, MARGARET 'Lord Sydenham's One Hundred and Fifteen Days in Kingston', *Historic Kingston*, 15 (1967), pp. 36–49

—— *The Old Stones of Kingston*, Toronto: University of Toronto Press, 1966

ARMSTRONG, R. FRASER 'An Experiment in Special Nursing, 1931', 'Kingston Community Hospital Plan, 1934–1941', *Project Series*, unpublished mss.

Brief of the College of Physicians and Surgeons of Ontario to the Ontario Committee on the Healing Arts, 1967.

BULL, WILLIAM PERKINS *From Medicine Man to Medical Man*, Toronto: G. J. McLeod, Ltd., 1934.

CAMPBELL, MARY C. *History of the Orphans' Home and Widows' Friend Society, 100 Years, 1857–1957*, Kingston, 1958.

—— *A Short History of the Women's Aid of the Kingston General Hospital, 1905–1968*, Kingston, 1969.

Canadian Hospital, vol. 37, no. 11 (November 1960).

Canadian Medical Association Journal.

CARELESS, J. M. S. & R. C. BROWN *The Canadians 1869–1967*, Toronto: Macmillan, 1967.

CANNIFF, WILLIAM *The Medical Profession in Upper Canada 1783–1850*, Toronto: W. Briggs, 1894.

CLARKE, C. K. *History of the Toronto General Hospital*, Toronto: W. Briggs, 1913

CONNELL, JAMES C. *History of the Kingston General Hospital*, Kingston, 1925 (4 pp.).

DUPUIS, NATHAN F. *A Sketch of the History of the Medical College at Kingston During the First Twenty-Five Years of Its Existence*, Kingston, 1916 (24 pp.).

EDMISON, J. ALEX 'History of the Kingston Penitentiary', *Historic Kingston*, 3, (1954), pp. 26–35.

FIFIELD, JAMES (ED.) *American and Canadian Hospitals*, Minneapolis: Midwest Publishers Co., 1933.

FLEXNER, ABRAHAM *Medical Education in the United States and Canada*, New York: Carnegie Foundation for the Advancement of Teaching, 1910.

GARRISON, FIELDING H. *Introduction to the History of Medicine*, Philadelphia: Saunders, 1929.

GIBBON, J. M. & M. S. MATHEWSON *Three Centuries of Canadian Nursing*, Toronto: Macmillan, 1947.

GIBSON, THOMAS 'Notes on the Medical History of Kingston', *Journal of the Canadian Medical Association*, 1928, pp. 331–334.

—— *A Short Account of the Development of Medical Teaching at Kingston*, Kingston, 1928.

GUNDY, H. PEARSON 'Growing Pains – The Early History of the Queen's Medical Faculty', *Historic Kingston*, 4 (1955), pp. 14–25.

—— *Queen's University at Kingston*, Kingston, 1968.

HEAGERTY, J. J. *Four Centuries of Medical History in Canada*, 2 vols. Toronto: Macmillan, 1928.

—— *Romance of Medicine in Canada*, Toronto: Ryerson, 1940.

HENRY, WALTER *Trifles From My Portfolio*, Quebec: Neilson, 1839.

HITSMAN, J. MACKAY *The Incredible War of 1812*, Toronto: University of Toronto Press, 1965.

HORSEY, EDWIN 'History of Kingston,' unpublished ms.

—— 'Care of the Sick and Hospitalization at Kingston, 1783–1938,' unpublished ms.

JONES, W. A. 'The Story of Radiology', Queen's Medical Centenary Series, *The Queen's Review*, vol. 29, no. 5 (May–June, 1954), 124–29.

Kingston Medical Quarterly, October 1896–October 1903.

LEWIS, D. SCLATER *The Royal College of Physicians and Surgeons of Canada*, Montreal: McGill University Press, 1962.

—— *History of the Royal Victoria Hospital 1887–1947*, Montreal: McGill University Press, 1969.

MACDERMOT, H. E. *History of the Canadian Medical Association*, vol. 1, 1935, vol. 2, 1955.

—— *A History of the Montreal General Hospital*, Montreal: Montreal General Hospital, 1950.

—— *One Hundred Years of Medicine in Canada 1867–1967*, Toronto: McClelland & Stewart, 1967.

NICKLE, HUGH 'History of the School of Nursing,' unpublished ms.

ONTARIO DEPARTMENT OF HEALTH *The Hospitals of Ontario*, Toronto 1934.

POWELL, ROBERT W. *A Doctor in Canada*, Montreal: *Gazette*, 1890.

PRESTON, RICHARD A. *Kingston Before the War of 1812*, Toronto: University of Toronto Press, 1959.

Queen's Medical Quarterly, October 1903–April 1909.

STERN, BERNARD J. *Society and Medical Progress*, Princeton: Princeton University Press, 1941.

SULLIVAN, MICHAEL 'Retrospect of 50 Years,' unpublished ms. (3 pp.).

WHITE, E. P. 'History of Urology in Canada', unpublished ms.

Illustrations

Aerial View
1969

Dr. James
Sampson

Dr. Horatio Yates

Original Building
and Watkins Wing
facing King Street

Watkins, Main and Nickle   1893

K.G.H. from the South with Fenwick Operating Theatre

Hospital Room
1906

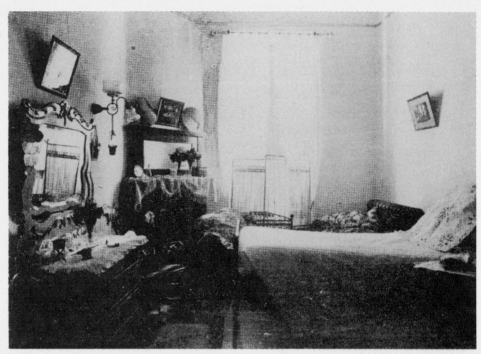

Hospital Room
1969

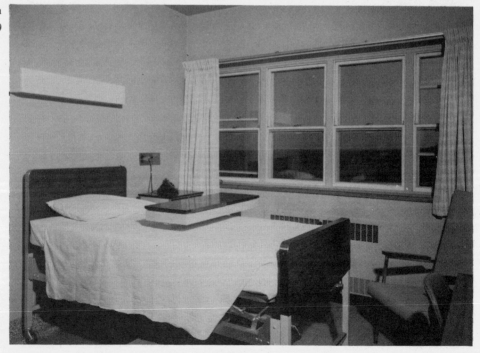

Fenwick
Operating Theatre
1895

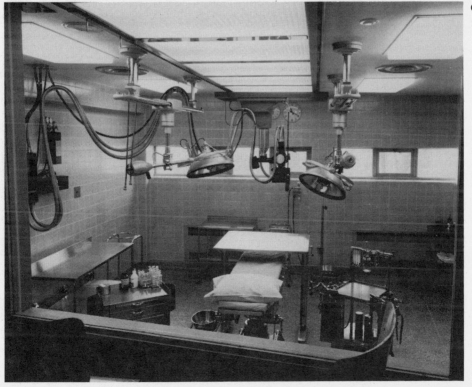

Operating Room
1969

Empire Wing

TOP
Nurses' Residence
1903

CENTRE
Nurses' Residence
1927

BOTTOM
Nurses' Residence
1969

Dr. Ephraim Hooper

Dr. Roland Kilborn

Dr. James Third

Fraser Armstrong

D. M. MacIntyre

Douglas Wing

Victory Wing

Angada Children's
Hospital

W. T. Connell
Wing

Dr. W. T. Connell

Dr. W. F. Connell